YA 2013? 2014? 2015? 2017? 2019?
Graphic Novel
Hulk

GIANT-SIZE
HULK

GIANT-SIZE HULK

cruz
ez

ligraphy's Randy Gentile
than Cosby
ia

EDIBLE HULK

'ury"

d & Cory Hamscher
Wayne Nichols
ndzierski
ire
dan D. White
ia

ast"
in
nual #7 (1978)

HULK: RAGING THUNDER

"Unbeatable"
Writer: Jeff Parker
Artist: Mitch Breitweiser
Colorist: Moose Baumann
Letterer: Blambot's Nate Piekos
Assistant Editor: Nathan Cosby
Editor: Mark Paniccia

"Thundra at Dawn"
originally presented in
Fantastic Four #133 (1973)
Writer: Gerry Conway
Penciler: Ramona Fradon
Inker: Joe Sinnott
Colorist: Stan Goldberg
Letterer: John Costanza
Plotter and Editor: Roy Thomas

HULK VS. HERCULES: WHEN TITANS COLLIDE

COLLECTION CREDITS

Collection Editor: Alex Starbuck
Assistant Editors: Cory Levine & John Denning
Editors, Special Projects: Jennifer Grünwald & Mark D. Beazley
Senior Editor, Special Projects: Jeff Youngquist
Senior Vice President of Sales: David Gabriel
Production: Jerry Kalinowski
Book Design: Spring Hoteling

Editor in Chief: Joe Quesada
Publisher: Dan Buckley

SOOK

SOME YEARS AGO, ON THE CAMPUS OF U.C.L.A....
THIS IS SPOONER...GIVE ME A SITREP, PLEASE.
EAGLE IS IN MOTION AND IS SLATED TO ARRIVE IN TWENTY MINUTES, REPEAT, TWENTY MINUTES. LET'S HAVE FINAL LOCKDOWN ON--

HO, AGENT SPOONER! WHAT CARE DOEST THOU HAVE FOR THE SAFETY OF THY CHARGE...
FREEZE--!

...WHEN THE SON OF ZEUS HIMSELF STANDS AGAINST ANY HARM THAT MIGHT BEFALL HIM!
THE SENTIMENT'S APPRECIATED, HERCULES, BUT WE STILL HAVE A JOB TO DO.

INDEED! PERHAPS THOU HAS FORGOTTEN...BUT THE PRESIDENT CHOOSES TO HONOR *US* FOR SAVING THE WORLD FROM THE EFFECTS OF DOCTOR DOOM'S MIND-CONTROL GAS!
WHERE WERT *THOU* WHEN THE CHAMPIONS *ALONE* STOOD BETWEEN DOOM AND WORLD DOMINATION LAST WEEK?
BENDING KNEE TO A TYRANT, METHINKS!
*IT HAPPENED IN CHAMPIONS #16! WHERE WERT THOU?--ED.

CUT THE GENTLEMAN SOME SLACK, HERCULES.

AS HE SAID, HE AND THE OTHER SECRET SERVICE AGENTS ARE JUST DOING THEIR JOBS, GETTING THE CAMPUS SECURED FOR PRESIDENT CLINTON'S ARRIVAL.
IT'S NOT EVERY DAY WE GET THE CONGRESSIONAL MEDAL OF HONOR.
ESPECIALLY FOR DEALING WITH A THREAT NOBODY WOULD HAVE EVEN REMEMBERED...
...IF GHOST RIDER HERE HADN'T FILLED US ALL IN.
ONE OF THE ADVANTAGES IN NOT HAVING TO BREATHE WHEN I'M GHOST RIDER.
"ONE?" WHAT *OTHER* ADVANTAGES ARE THERE, JOHNNY BLAZE?
WELL...I DON'T HAVE TO SMELL MY OWN FACE *BURNING*. THAT'S A PLUS.
"CLINTON?" STRANGE. I THOUGHT THE PRESIDENT'S NAME WAS "*CARTER...*"
DOOM'S GAS MUST'VE SCRAMBLED YOUR BRAIN, HERC. CARTER WAS PRESIDENT BACK WHEN I WAS IN DIAPERS.
AYE, OF COURSE, ICEMAN. WHEN ONE IS IMMORTAL, THE NAMES TEND TO RUN TOGETHER.

SAY AGAIN? DO WE HAVE VERIFICATION ON THAT?
BLAST! ALL RIGHT, ALERT ALL UNITS WE HAVE A CODE JADE, REPEAT, CODE JADE...
AND WHAT MIGHT A "CODE JADE" BE, AGENT SPOONER? CAN WE HELP?
ACTUALLY, BLACK WIDOW, YOU MAY BE ABLE TO AT THAT.
WE HAVE TRAFFIC SHUT DOWN BOTH WAYS ON THE 405 SO THE PRESIDENT'S MOTORCADE CAN COME THROUGH.
WE HAVE A BELIEVED SIGHTING OF DOCTOR BRUCE BANNER IN A SILVER DELOREAN, SITTING IN TRAFFIC ONE MILE SOUTH OF THE WILSHIRE BOULEVARD EXIT!
BRUCE BANNER? THE HULK?
IS THERE ANY OTHER WE'D BE WORRIED ABOUT?
THEN WORRY NO MORE. WE'RE ON IT.
WH--
ANGEL! GET BACK HERE IMMEDIATELY!
RELAX, 'TASHA. I'M JUST GOING TO VERIFY THE SIGHTING. I'D RECOGNIZE BANNER FROM A MILE AWAY.
IT'S NOT LIKE I HAVE ANY INTENTION OF GETTING INTO A DUSTUP WITH THE HULK.
NO ONE EVER DOES. THAT'S HOW IT STARTS.

I KNOW WHY SPOONER AND COMPANY ARE JUMPY. THE HULK WAS A VICTIM OF DOOM'S MIND-CONTROL GAS, AND WE WOUND UP SLUGGING IT OUT WITH HIM.
FOR ALL WE KNOW, IT'S STILL RATTLING AROUND IN HIS SKULL. AND IF HE'S MAKING A BEELINE FOR THE PRESIDENT...
...WE HAVE TO HEAD IT OFF, FAST.
AT LEAST HE'S IN SOMETHING DISTINCTIVE. UNLESS THERE'S A "BACK TO THE FUTURE" CONVENTION IN TOWN, HOW MANY DELOREANS CAN THERE B--
AHA!
A MILE SOUTH OF WILSHIRE AS THE ANGEL FLIES.
THAT'S GOT TO BE HIM...
GOT TO GET CLOSE ENOUGH TO MAKE CERTAIN OF--
RAARRRRRR
OHHHH, THAT DOESN'T SOUND GOOD.

STUPID CAR...!
HULK CANNOT DO WHAT HULK MUST DO...
...STUCK IN STUPID, STUPID CAR!
GREEN PIECES
PETER DAVID WRITER
JUAN SANTACRUZ PENCILER
RAUL FERNANDEZ INKER
STUDIO F COLORISTS
VC'S RANDY GENTILE LETTERER
NATHAN COSBY ASSISTANT EDITOR
MARK PANICCIA EDITOR
JOE QUESADA EDITOR IN CHIEF
DAN BUCKLEY PUBLISHER

THIS IS ANGEL! IT'S HIM, ALL RIGHT!
ANGEL, THIS IS ICEMAN. YOU SURE?
OF COURSE I'M SURE! WHO ELSE WEARS PURPLE PANTS AFTER LABOR DAY?
BESIDES, HE JUST TURNED BIG AND GREEN!
YOU MEAN HE'S BECOME THE HULK?!
NO, HE'S HAVING AN ALLERGIC REACTION TO CHIVES! YES, YOU DOPE, THAT'S WHAT I MEAN!
WE'RE ON OUR WAY! STALL HIM!
STALL HIM?! HOW? MOLT ON HIM?
OKAY, HULK! STAY RIGHT WHERE YOU ARE, OR--!
OR WHAT, BIRD MAN?
YEAH, I'M KIND OF HAZY ON THAT MYSELF.
HULK HAS NO TIME FOR THIS. HULK NEED TO BE...
...SOMEWHERE.
WHOA! THAT WAS CLOSER THAN I NEEDED IT TO--

OH NO!
CONGRATULATIONS!
HAPPY HONEYMOON!
OUT OF THE WAY! WATCH OUT!
OOOOOFFF!!

HULK NEEDS TO BE...DOING SOMETHING...
CAN'T REMEMBER... WHY IS HULK HERE? WHY...?
WAIT...HULK... REMEMBERS NOW...
YOU SEE HIM? HE SHOULD BE JUST UP AHEAD.
NOT YET! MAYBE HE'S LEFT THE--
NO! WAIT! THERE HE IS!
TRANS
FLAME HEAD AND ICE MAN SHOULD GET OUT OF HERE! OR HULK WILL DO TO THEM WHAT HE DID TO WING MAN!
18-909

LEARN OUR NAMES, WHY DON'T'CHA?! IT'S NOT "WING MAN," IT'S ANGEL! IT'S NOT "FLAME HEAD," IT'S GHOST RIDER! AND IT'S NOT ICE MAN, IT'S--
UHM...OKAY. YEAH. IT'S "ICEMAN."
WOW. NEVER REALIZED HOW OBVIOUS MY NAME IS BEFORE.
NOT TOO CLOSE, GHOST TOASTY! WOULDN'T WANT THAT FLAME TRAIL OF YOURS TO MELT MY SPECIAL-MADE HULKSICLE!
HOW LONG DO YOU EXPECT THAT WILL HOLD HIM?
A FEW MINUTES, I GUESS...

KRSHHHH!!!
GUESS AGAIN!
LET'S GO TO EXTREMES, SHALL WE? A BLAST OF HELLFIRE SHOULD--
--MISS YOU COMPLETELY...
HULK WANTS YOU *OUT* OF HULK'S WAY! WHAT DOES HULK HAVE TO DO TO MAKE STUPID HEROES *UNDERSTAND?*
FOR STARTERS, HULK, YOU CAN DROP THE CAR AND SURRENDER TO THE CHAMPIONS!
MUCH THANKS FOR THE TRANSPORT ASSIST, FAIR LAYNIA!
THE POWER OF THE DARKSTAR IS AT YOUR SERVICE AS ALWAYS, HERCULES.

YOU ONLY RECEIVE ONE WARNING, HULK!
STUPID GAS... MAKES HULK'S EYES HURT!
HULK MAKE YOU HURT ALL OVER!
STAY BACK, NATASHA! I WILL NOT HAVE HIM HAMPERED BY THE LIKES OF TEAR GAS!
SUCH A *WORTHY* FOE DESERVES THE UNFETTERED GIFT OF BATTLE FROM THE SON OF ZEUS!
PUT *DOWN* THINE AUTOMOTIVE WEAPON, GREEN ONE!
FIGHT INSTEAD WITH YOUR FISTS, AS BEFITS A--

DOES SKIRT MAN EVER SHUT UP!?!
"SKIRT MAN"? ZOUNDS. METHINKS I WILL NOT BE HEARING THE END OF *THAT* ANYTIME SOON.

DARKSTAR, HOLD HIM STEADY! GHOST RIDER, ICEMAN, FROM EITHER SIDE... TAKE HIM! NOW!
ARRRRRR!
LET HULK GO!!!
NOT A CHANCE, YOU MONOSYLLABIC MONSTER!
I KNOW THINKING ISN'T YOUR STRONG SUIT, HULKSTER, BUT EVEN YOU SHOULD'VE KNOWN BETTER THAN TO PRESS YOUR LUCK WITH THE CHAMPIONS!
YOU THINK HULK IS STUPID... BECAUSE OF WAY HULK TALKS!
BECAUSE OF WHAT...HULK DOES!

YOU THINK... YOU KNOW... EVERYTHING!
YOU--
--KNOW--
--NOTHING!!!

BUT NOW ONE THING YOU *DO* KNOW.
YOU KNOW HULK IS STRONGEST ONE THERE IS.
YOU *REMEMBER* THAT...
...OR HULK WILL SMASH YOU A SECOND TIME!
CURIOUS. HE NEVER ACTUALLY HURLED THE VEHICLE *AT* US.
ANGEL? WARREN, DO YOU COPY?
I'M HERE, BOSS LADY. KINDA BRUISED AND PICKING GLASS OUT OF MY WINGS, BUT OKAY OTHERWISE.
THE HULK'S HEADING NORTH. CAN YOU FOLLOW HIM?
HE'S KIND OF HARD TO MISS.
HE'S COMING DOWN. I THINK HE'S...
YEAH. HE'S LANDED. AND HE'S...
WHAT THE HECK...?
WARREN? WHAT'S *HAPPENING?*
HE...

HE...HE'S OUTSIDE CEDAR-SINAI HOSPITAL... THE EMERGENCY ENTRANCE...
WHERE IS DOCTOR!?
OHHHHH GOD...BRUCE, IT HURTS...!
STUPID DOCTOR GET HERE NOW, OR HULK WILL BRING WHOLE STUPID BUILDING DOWN!
YOU HEARD THE... UH...THE MAN!
THE LADY OBVIOUSLY NEEDS SOME ASSISTANCE.
PAIN IN THE LOWER RIGHT ABDOMEN! COULD BE APPENDICITIS!
GUT...ON FIRE...!
PREP O.R. THREE FOR A POSSIBLE EMERGENCY APPENDECTOMY!
WOW.
HULK, YOU MAY HAVE GOTTEN HER HERE JUST IN--
--TIME.

MY NAME IS JENNIFER WALTERS. I'M BRUCE BANNER'S COUSIN. I'M AN ATTORNEY HERE IN L.A.
HE WAS VISITING ME.
THE SECRET SERVICE WANTS TO KNOW WHY.
BECAUSE HE LIKES ME, AND VICE VERSA. HE'S MY COUSIN, FOR PITY'S SAKE.
WE WERE STUCK IN TRAFFIC AND SUDDENLY I FELT LIKE MY INSIDES WERE EXPLODING. I GUESS HE GOT WORRIED, UPSET...AND THAT CAUSED HIM TO, YOU KNOW...
BUT HE STILL RETAINED ENOUGH OF HIS PERSONALITY AS BRUCE--EVEN AS THE HULK--TO WANT TO TRY AND GET ME TO A HOSPITAL.
TURNED OUT MY APPENDIX RUPTURED. IF WE'D GOTTEN HERE FIVE MINUTES LATER, I WOULD'VE BEEN A GONER.
BUT IF THAT WAS HIS INTENT... WHY DID HE NOT TELL US?
DID YOU ASK?
STOP

THE OFFICE OF THE PRESIDENT CALLED. THEY WANTED TO ARRANGE ANOTHER DATE FOR THE MEDAL CEREMONY...
...SINCE THE PRESIDENT WAS WHISKED OUT OF THE AREA THE MOMENT A FIGHT BROKE OUT.
TELL THEM TO GIVE THEIR MEDALS TO THOSE WHO ARE WORTHY.
OH, COME ON, HERCULES. CONSIDERING THE CIRCUMSTANCES...
THE CIRCUMSTANCES, BEAUTEOUS ONE, ARE THAT WE ARE SUPPOSED TO BE THE CHAMPIONS OF PEOPLE IN NEED.
YET THERE WAS THE HULK, IN NEED, AND WE SIMPLY ATTACKED.
YES...I KNOW. IVAN UNLOADED ON ME WHEN HE FOUND OUT. HE SAID, "HOW MANY TIMES DID I TELL YOU WHEN YOU WERE GROWING UP: NEVER ASSUME. IT MAKES AN ASS OF YOU AND ME."
THE HULK WAS RIGHT. WE KNEW NOTHING. AND WE ACTED ON THAT LACK OF KNOWLEDGE. A MISTAKE I SHALL NOT REPEAT. AND HOPEFULLY, ON SOME FUTURE DATE...
"...WE SHALL HAVE THE OPPORTUNITY TO MAKE AMENDS."
END.

HULK?! WHOA--PEACE, BROTHER!
IT'S ME-- FRED! DON'T FREAK--!

HULK?
TINK

YOU IMPRESS ME, SIR! AT MY LAST PERFORMANCE, SEVERAL STRONG MEN FAINTED DEAD AWAY AT THE VERY SIGHT OF MY ROBOTIC ASSOCIATE!
UH-HUH... ROBOT...

...SO, YOU MUST BE KROPOTKIN THE GREAT!
AT YOUR SERVICE. AND YOU ARE...?
FRED SLOAN--

--I CALLED ABOUT AN INTERVIEW?
AH, YES! YOU WISH TO HEAR OF MY ADVENTURES WITH THE TRUE INCREDIBLE HULK! A GRAND TALE IT IS...

"IT BEGAN WITH AN UNFORTUNATE MISUNDERSTANDING. DOCTOR ROBERT BRUCE BANNER CAME TO BE DOMICILED IN AN APARTMENT THAT I THOUGHT MINE ALONE...
DEFEND YOURSELF, SIR! YOU WILL KEEP MY PRECIOUS BELONGINGS OVER MY DEAD BODY!
"IN RETROSPECT, A FOOLHARDY CHALLENGE. AS BANNER'S YOUNG FRIEND, JAMES WILSON, SOON INFORMED ME.
"I DOUBTED HIS TALE AT FIRST. BUT SOON AFTER, I ACCOMPANIED JAMES TO THE CAMPUS OF BANNER'S ALMA MATER... AND THERE BEHELD THE AWESOME POWER OF THE HULK MYSELF!
KNOW THYSELF
"FORTUNATELY, HIS RAGE WAS SPENT UPON A MARBLE STATUE OF SOCRATES.
"AND THUS SATIATED--
"--THE MONSTER AGAIN BECAME MAN.
"AFTER THAT, WE WERE ALL WHISKED AWAY FOR DEBRIEFING AT THE GOVERNMENT'S GAMMA BASE.
" 'TWAS THERE THAT I HAD THE SINGULAR HONOR OF WITNESSING DOCTOR LEONARD SAMSON'S ATTEMPT TO DEAL WITH THE HULK'S... UNIQUE MIND..."

WAIT! DOC SAMSON PSYCHOANALYZED THE HULK?! WHAT DID HE LEARN?
EH? OH...

...SOMETHING ABOUT BANNER AND THE HULK BEING TWO SEPARATE PERSONAE.

I CANNOT RECALL THE SPECIFICS. THE MILITARY KEPT ME ISOLATED FROM SAMSON AND THE HULK.
THEY DOUBTED MY CLOSE PERSONAL RELATIONSHIP WITH DOCTOR BANNER, AND REGARDED ME AS SOME MANNER OF SECURITY RISK! I, WHO HAVE PERFORMED BEFORE HEADS OF STATE! THE VERY IDEA!
I WAS SOON FORCED TO EXIT THE BASE...
...BUT ON MY WAY OUT, I ACQUIRED THIS MAGNIFICENT TEST ROBOT.
CAN YOU BELIEVE THEY WERE DISCARDING IT?
SO, YOU HAVEN'T SEEN THE HULK SINCE?
KLIK
ALAS, NO. BUT OUR BRIEF ASSOCIATION GREATLY BENEFITED MY ACT.

I should have known. Kropotkin's just using the Hulk to line his pockets.
Am I any better?
Yes! I'm going to tell the Hulk's story. That'll help him...

...wherever he is out there.
WELCOME TO *COW-A-BUN-GA!* MAY I TAKE YOUR ORDER?
COW-A-BUN-GA
...PROTESTING DEVELOPMENT IN THE SAN MINGO MOUNTAINS.
A KAHUNA SUPREME AND A LITTLE SURFER MEAL.
SAN MINGO... WHY'S THAT SOUND FAMILIAR...?
EVERYBODY HUG THE FLOOR! NOW!
OH, NO...
WHAT'RE YOU, *DEAF?* THE FLOOR-- *NOW!*
YOU... *SHOULDN'T*... HAVE DONE THAT...

WHERE IS HULK?!
HULK SMELLS FOOD!
$@%#!
G-GET BACK! GET BACK OR--!
BUDA-BUDA-BUDA
GUNS?
HULK HATES GUNS!!
KREEESH
COW-A-BUNGA

PEOPLE LEAVE FOOD BEHIND? MMRPH! HULK'S FOOD NOW!
M-MISTER HULK? PLEASE ENJOY THIS COMPLIMENTARY PARTY-PAK. TO GO.
IF... YOU DON'T MIND... GOING?
HE...HE'S NOT GOING TO EAT US, IS HE?
BAH!
HULK WILL FIND BETTER PLACE!
KTHAM
JOANIE? CALL 9-1-1.
COW-A-BUN-GA
AND MY INSURANCE AGENT.
OHHH...
There are a lot of stories about the Hulk...

have had contact with him over the years...
CAPTAIN ANDERSON--!

CALL ME DAVE. I HAVEN'T BEEN CAPTAIN ANDERSON IN A LONG TIME.
OKAY. YOU WERE HEAD OF SECURITY AT LOS DIABLOS MISSILE BASE WHEN THE HULK FIRST SHOWED UP.

YEAH. IF I'D DONE A BETTER JOB, THAT MONSTER WOULD NEVER HAVE BEEN BORN.
YOU BLAME YOURSELF? THERE WERE REPORTS OF SABOTAGE--!
IT ALL HAPPENED ON MY WATCH. I WAS RESPONSIBLE...

"NO ONE SHOULD HAVE GOTTEN WITHIN TEN MILES OF THE GAMMA TOWER. BUT SOMEHOW, THAT KID--RICK JONES--GOT PAST ALL THE GUARDS AND FENCES.

"IF NOT FOR DOCTOR BANNER, JONES WOULD HAVE FRIED.
"I DON'T REMEMBER HOW MANY RADS THE DOC TOOK--

"--BUT HE WAS STILL SCREAMING WHEN WE FOUND THEM.
HELP HIM! YA GOTTA HELP HIM!

"THE NEXT NIGHT, WE HAD OUR FIRST ENCOUNTER WITH THE HULK. HE WRECKED THE BASE HOSPITAL, TOTALED AN ARMORED HUMVEE, AND INJURED FOUR OF MY BEST MEN."

SOMETHING I'VE ALWAYS WONDERED, DAVE...WHY WAS HE CALLED "THE HULK"?

THAT'S WHAT THE NON-COMS NAMED HIM. SEEMED TO FIT.
I WASN'T WITNESS TO THAT FIRST RUN-IN...

"...BUT I WAS THERE FOR THE AFTERMATH. IT WAS LIKE A WAR ZONE. TWO-FOOT THICK WALLS OF REINFORCED CONCRETE HAD BEEN PUNCHED THROUGH!
"THERE WAS NO SIGN OF BANNER OR JONES. I WAS AFRAID THE HULK HAD ABDUCTED THEM...AND IN A WAY, I GUESS HE DID.

"THE PATH OF DESTRUCTION LED US TO A RANSACKED LABORATORY, WHERE WE FOUND BANNER, JONES, AND A LAB TECH NAMED IGOR DRENKOV.
"DRENKOV WAS OUR SABOTEUR. FOR A WHILE I THOUGHT THAT HE WAS IN LEAGUE WITH THE HULK.

REALLY? YOU NEVER SUSPECTED BANNER--?
I SUSPECTED ANYONE AND EVERYONE-- THAT'S THE JOB. BUT BANNER...
...WHEN I FIRST QUESTIONED HIM ABOUT THE HULK, HE HAD NO IDEA WHAT I WAS TALKING ABOUT. HE SEEMED DAZED... DISORIENTED.
UH-HUH. AND WHAT COLOR WAS THE HULK THAT FIRST NIGHT? I'VE READ THAT SOMEONE DESCRIBED HIM AS GRAY-SKINNED.
AS I SAID, I WASN'T THERE. IT HAPPENED VERY QUICKLY, IN THE DEAD OF NIGHT. AND, NOT SURPRISINGLY, OUR EYEWITNESSES GAVE CONFLICTING REPORTS.

"BUT WHEN I FIRST SAW THE HULK, HE WAS DEFINITELY GREEN!
"WE HAD TRACKED HIM TO GENERAL ROSS'S OWN QUARTERS. ROSS WAS SO HOT TO CATCH THE MONSTER THAT HE SENT A TANK SMASHING INTO THE PLACE.
"THE HULK WAS...HUGE...

"...SO BIG, HE DIDN'T SEEM REAL! MAYBE THAT'S WHY THE TROOPS JUMPED HIM.
"BEFORE I COULD ORDER THEM BACK, A DOZEN MEN PILED ON THE HULK. HE JUST SHRUGGED--

"--AND SENT THEM FLYING! THEN HE RIPPED UP ONE SIDE OF THE BUILDING AND WAS GONE.

"ROSS WAS LIVID. SWORE HE WOULDN'T REST UNTIL THE HULK WAS CAPTURED. I REMEMBER HIM BROWBEATING BANNER...DEMANDING THAT THE DOC FIND SOME WAY TO STOP THE HULK."

WE DIDN'T KNOW THEN THAT BANNER WAS THE HULK. I DIDN'T FIND OUT UNTIL MONTHS LATER. BY THEN I'D BEEN TRANSFERRED TO ANOTHER BASE.
I NEVER SAW HIM OR THE HULK AGAIN, EXCEPT ON TV.
AND IN MY NIGHTMARES...

THANKS FOR YOUR TIME, DAVE. I'VE LEARNED A LOT.
ANDERSON
JUST TELL THE TRUTH. NOTHING ELSE MATTERS.

I keep seeing that haunted look in Anderson's eyes. I must use his story in the book--
--He's an important link to the Hulk's past.

And he's right, I have to tell the truth--warts and all--if I want people to really understand the Hulk...

...if *I* want to really understand him!
MMM...FOOD GOOD...
HONK-HONK!
EH?
NOW WHO IS SPOILING HULK'S MEAL?!

HARVEY, JUST GO AROUND THE BEAR.
I CAN'T. THERE'S--
HONK-HONK!
ENOUGH!
--NO ROOM.
THOOM!

GO AWAY!!
GOOD! SMART BEAR.
HONK
HARVEY, LET UP ON THE HORN!
...
HULK SAID--
HONK!

--ENOUGH!!
HULK CHASES BEAR AWAY--
KUH-CHOOM
--AND STILL PUNY HUMANS MAKE NOISE?!
I-I-I'M SORRY. I PANICKED.
PLEASE DON'T HURT US.
BAH! HULK WILL GO SOMEWHERE QUIET...
I know the Hulk has caused a lot of damage over the years...

...But it seems that there's a more human toll...
SO, MR. MORAN...I HEAR YOU SAW THE HULK--!
YOU BELIEVE THAT?
NOT MANY PEOPLE DO.
BUT ONCE UPON A TIME, MY WORD MEANT SOMETHIN'...
"I WAS TOP SALESMAN IN THE STATE--PULLIN' IN SIX FIGURES A YEAR! MAN, I HAD IT MADE!"
...AND A KING...I'VE BEEN UP AND DOWN AND--
"THEN IT ALL FELL APART. IF ONLY I HADN'T GLANCED UP."
--OVER AND...
...OUT?
"BUT I DID. AND THAT CHANGED EVERYTHING...
SO...YOU WERE WATCHING A LITTLE GREEN MAN--!
YES... NO! HE WAS BIG!

"THE MORE I TRIED TO EXPLAIN, THE WORSE IT GOT. NO ONE BELIEVED ME. NOT THE POLICE, NOT MY FRIENDS, NOT EVEN MY FAMILY...
BUT IT'S TRUE--!
SON, YOU NEED HELP!
RAY, YOU'VE GOTTA BE THE BIGGEST LIAR IN THE ENTIRE NEIGHBORHOOD!
"AND FROM THE MILITARY, ALL I GOT WAS--"
THAT'S TOP SECRET.
"I SPENT YEARS SEARCHING FOR PROOF. BUT I FOUND TOO LITTLE..."
- HULK
CLASSIFIED
...AND TOO LATE. I LOST MY CAR, MY JOB, MY WIFE.
I'M SORRY.
I'M SURE DR. BANNER WOULD BE, TOO.
DON'T GIVE ME THAT! HE'S A MONSTER! HE WRECKED MY LIFE!
UH...
Ray Moran brought most of that on himself. But it makes me wonder... does anyone have a good word for the Hulk?
EXIT

Is there no one who truly cares?
The Daily Grind
ALL RIGHT, MR. SLOAN, I'M ON BREAK--

--AND ALL YOURS FOR THE NEXT 20 MINUTES.
THANKS, MARIA.

THANK *YOU!* THIS IS SO EXCITING! I'VE NEVER BEEN INTERVIEWED BY AN AUTHOR BEFORE!
HOW OLD WERE YOU WHEN YOU SAW THE HULK?
-MMPH- TEN AND A HALF. I'LL NEVER FORGET IT...

"OUR BUS HAD BROKEN DOWN RIGHT IN THE MIDDLE OF A RAILROAD CROSSING, AND A *TRAIN* WAS BEARING DOWN ON US. THERE WAS NO TIME TO GET OUT.
SCHOOL

"I'D STARTED TO PRAY, WHEN I SAW HIM. HE DROPPED FROM THE SKY LIKE A BIG BIRD!

"HE JUST *LIFTED* US OFF THE TRACKS!

"AND THEN, HE WAS GONE.
"OUR BUS DRIVER NEVER EVEN SAW HIM...
"...BUT *I* DID."

OF COURSE, I WAS JUST A LITTLE GIRL...NO ONE BELIEVED ME THEN. THE AUTHORITIES SAID I WAS HYSTERICAL. BUT I KNEW BETTER.
YES, WELL...AT THAT TIME, THE GOVERNMENT WAS STILL TRYING TO KEEP THE HULK'S EXISTENCE UNDER WRAPS. THEY WERE TRYING TO PREVENT A PANIC...
I KNOW. LOTS OF PEOPLE ARE AFRAID OF THE HULK. THEY THINK HE'S A MONSTER.
BUT TO ME, HE'S A BIG, GREEN ANGEL.

I'M GLAD TO HEAR YOU SAY THAT, MARIA. I WAS BEGINNING TO THINK IT WAS JUST ME.
I'VE MET THE HULK, MYSELF...
QUE?

"...OUTSIDE A LITTLE TAVERN IN NORTHERN CALIFORNIA. I WAS ON THE WRONG END OF A... CULTURAL DISAGREEMENT... AND THE HULK DECIDED TO TAKE MY SIDE.

ALL I WANTED WAS ANOTHER LOUSY BEER, BUT YOU DIDN'T WANT THAT, DIDJA? YOU WERE TIRED OF SERVING "THE HIPPIE"...YOU WANTED TO *FIGHT!*
WELL, WHAT'RE YOU *WAITING* FOR? *LET'S FIGHT!* ME AND MY BUDDY HERE WILL TAKE YOU ALL ON!
"NOBODY ACCEPTED.
"THE NEXT DAY, I GAVE THE HULK A RIDE THROUGH THE MOUNTAINS--

"--AND AS HE RELAXED, HE TURNED BACK INTO BRUCE BANNER. BUT WE DIDN'T GET TO TALK MUCH. THINGS...INTERVENED.

"LET'S JUST SAY THAT THE HULK GOT ME OUT OF SOME TOUGH SCRAPES. I OWE HIM... BIG TIME."

WOW! IT SOUNDS LIKE YOU KNOW THE HULK A LOT BETTER THAN I DO.
YEAH. I GUESS I DO.
BUT I STILL DON'T KNOW AS MUCH AS I'D LIKE TO! THAT'S WHY I'M DOING THESE INTERVIEWS.
SEE, I'M WRITING THIS BOOK TO HELP PEOPLE UNDERSTAND THE HULK, SO THEY'LL LET HIM LIVE IN PEACE...
YEAH...!
And that's when it hit me...

SAY AGAIN, FRED? YOU'RE BREAKING UP...
SORRY, CHRISTINE. THE SIGNAL'S A LITTLE WEAK OUT HERE.
OUT WHERE?
THE SAN MINGO MOUNTAINS. HULK AND I CAME THROUGH HERE ONCE. I REMEMBER HIM SAYING IT WAS ONE OF HIS FAVORITE PLACES...
...A QUIET SPOT WHERE HE COULD BE ALONE. IT'S A LONG SHOT, BUT IF I CAN FIND HIM AND TALK TO HIM--!
YOU INTEND TO INTERVIEW THE HULK--?!
YOU DON'T HAVE TO MAKE IT SOUND SO CRAZY.
IT IS CRAZY!
END CORPORATE GREED!
KEEP OUT!
AMERICA'S FORESTS AMERICA'S LUNGS
HEY, YOU'RE MY EDITOR! I THOUGHT YOU'D--!
HOLD ON...

HEY, BRO, WHAT'S WITH THE FENCE?
SCHIST CONSTRUCTION IS CLEAR-CUTTING THE FOREST TO BUILD MORE MCMANSIONS!
END
WE'RE TRYING TO GET AN INJUNCTION, BUT BY THE TIME THE COURTS--!
BOOM
UH-OH...
END

...Found him.
NO MORE!
MEN HAVE CUT DOWN ENOUGH TREES!
PUNY HUMANS NEVER KNOW WHEN TO STOP!
BUT THE HULK WILL STOP THEM!
KER-TOOM

HONK-HONK! HONK!
HULK--!
KTOOM

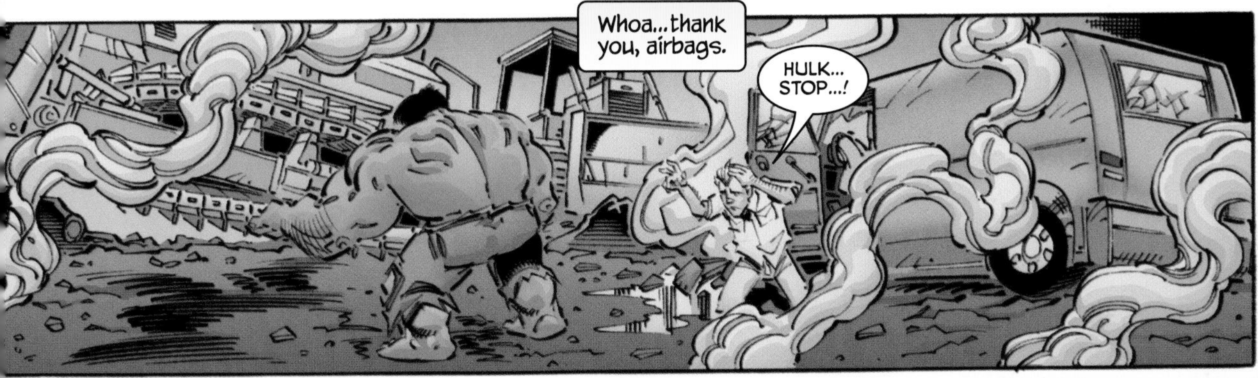
Whoa...thank you, airbags.
HULK... STOP...!

NO ONE TELLS HULK WHAT TO DO!
HULK, NO! IT'S ME--IT'S FRED!
PEACE, BROTHER! DON'T FREAK OUT!
PLEASE...?

FRED!
HEY...BIG GUY.
FRED IS HURT--!
JUST SHAKEN A LITTLE...I'LL BE OKAY.
WEEEOOOOO
SIRENS! HULK WILL *SMASH* PUNY--!
HULK, *NO!*
YOU GOTTA GET OUTTA HERE! IF THE COPS SEE YOU, THEY'LL START SHOOTING. SOMEONE COULD GET HURT-- MAYBE *ME!*
YOU DON'T WANT THAT...DO YOU?
NO! FRED IS HULK'S FRIEND...
--HEAR ME, FRED? ARE YOU ALL RIGHT?
EVERYTHING'S OKAY, CHRIS. FOR NOW.
Look at him go. I bet he covers a mile with each leap.

At that rate, he'll reach the coast by sunset.
KTOOM!
WHY?!?
WHY DOES HULK ALWAYS HURT HIS FRIENDS?
WHY?
"I'M SORRY IT DIDN'T WORK OUT...

EMERGENCY
...I MEAN--!
I KNOW. COULD HAVE BEEN THE INTERVIEW OF THE CENTURY.
WHAT I COULD HEAR OVER THE PHONE WAS *TERRIFYING!* HE WOULD HAVE *KILLED* YOU!
NO...

...AS SOON AS HULK SAW IT WAS ME, HE STOPPED. HE RECOGNIZED ME, CHRISTINE. HE REMEMBERED ME AS HIS FRIEND.
SURE, HE CAN BE DANGEROUS--
I'LL SAY!
--BUT HE ISN'T EVIL OR CRUEL. AND HE *CARES* ABOUT HIS FRIENDS, AS FEW AS HE MAY HAVE.
I UNDERSTAND WHY HE SCARES YOU. HE STILL SCARES *ME...*

"...I ONCE SAW HIM RIP APART A SOLID OAK TABLE AS IF IT WERE STYROFOAM!
"HE'S LIKE A BIG, GREEN RAMPAGING *ID.* BUT YOU KNOW...

...I ONCE CAME UPON AN OLD PROVERB..."WITHIN EACH OF US, OFTTIMES THERE DWELLS A MIGHTY RAGING FURY."
DOC BANNER'S FURY JUST HAPPENS TO HAVE BECOME A SEPARATE BEING. AND NEITHER OF THEM HAS ANY SAY IN THE MATTER. THAT'S WHY I WANT TO TELL THEIR STORY.
BETTER YOU THAN ME. HERE...

HUH? IS THIS MARKETING'S IDEA OF A GOOD COVER?!

DID THEY HAVE TO MAKE THE HULK LOOK SO FEROCIOUS?
HULK
ENCOUNTER
SURVIVOR'S STORY

AND THE TITLE! THE BOOK ISN'T ABOUT ME!
RELAX, IT'S JUST A ROUGH.
A LOT CAN HAPPEN BETWEEN NOW AND DEADLINE.

A LOT ALREADY HAS.
Los Angeles
400 Miles
I'm trying to do right by you, Hulk. This book could change things for both of us. I wonder...

...where are you bedding down tonight?
And what will tomorrow bring?
UH...?
WHERE HAVE YOU BROUGHT ME THIS TIME, HULK?
IS THAT...THE PACIFIC?

YES, BY THE LOOK OF THINGS...I MUST BE SOMEWHERE IN SOUTHERN CALIFORNIA.

CAREFUL! STEP ONE--AVOID THE BICYCLE COP. STEP TWO--

TOGS & SUCH
--FIND BETTER CLOTHES.

EXCUSE ME! ARE YOU OPENING--?
YEAH... WHOA! ROUGH NIGHT?

UH...YEAH. THIS IS EMBARRASSING. GUESS I SLEPT IT OFF UNDER THE PIER.
HEY, BEEN *THERE,* MAN!
UH-HUH. ANYWAY, I NEED NEW CLOTHES... AND SUCH. I HAVE ***TRAVELERS CHECKS.*** THEY'RE A LITTLE DAMP...
HEY, NO PROBLEM!
OPEN
NICE OF HIM TO LET ME USE THEIR WASHROOM.
NOTHING TO DO NOW BUT--

"--START ALL OVER. AGAIN."
UHHN? WHERE ARE WE?
MORNING, SLEEPY HEAD--
--WE'RE IN LONG BEACH, NOT FAR FROM MY OFFICE. WANT TO STOP FOR COFFEE?
SURE...
...COFFEE SOUNDS GOOD.
As I slept, I dreamt about the Hulk.
Does **he** dream? If he sleeps--if he totally relaxes--he usually turns back into Doctor Banner.
That's the real hell of it. Banner doesn't get to stay angry... and the Hulk doesn't get to be happy.
Like it or not, they're **stuck** with each other.
And who knows when-- or **if**-- it will ever **end?**

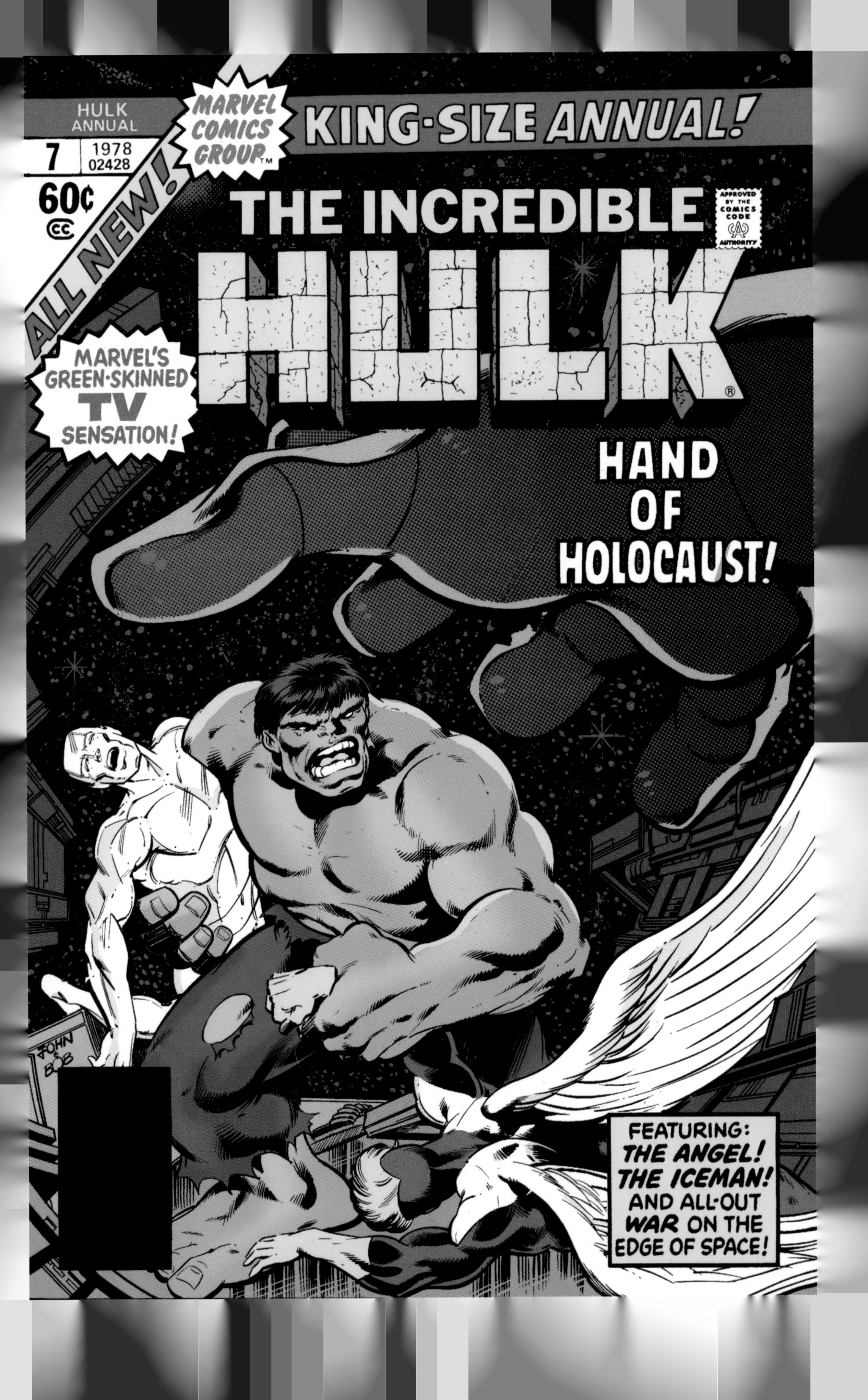
HULK ANNUAL
7
1978
02428
60¢
MARVEL COMICS GROUP
KING-SIZE ANNUAL!
ALL NEW!
THE INCREDIBLE
HULK
MARVEL'S GREEN-SKINNED TV SENSATION!
HAND OF HOLOCAUST!
JOHN & BOB
FEATURING:
THE ANGEL!
THE ICEMAN!
AND ALL-OUT
WAR ON THE
EDGE OF SPACE!

Stan Lee PRESENTS: THE INCREDIBLE HULK!®
ROGER STERN & JOHN BYRNE WRITER PENCILER CO-PLOTTERS
BOB LAYTON INKER
JIM NOVAK LETTERER
JANICE COHEN COLORIST
BOB HALL EDITOR
JIM SHOOTER EDITOR-IN-CHIEF

"THE EVIL THAT IS CAST..."
GOOD EVENING!
WORD COMES TONIGHT FROM NEW MEXICO'S GAMMA BASE THAT DR. ROBERT BRUCE BANNER-- BETTER KNOWN AS THE INCREDIBLE HULK-- HAS TURNED HIMSELF IN TO AUTHORITIES FOR TREATMENT.
HERE NOW WITH THAT LIVE REPORT IS CORRESPONDENT CHARLES P. IRWIN--
AH, BUT LIFE IS GOOD TO THE IDLE RICH! TAKE WARREN WORTHINGTON, FOR INSTANCE...

...HE HAS A SUMMER HOME IN THE ROCKIES, WITH ALL THE LUXURIES! HE ALSO HAS A PAIR OF VERY REAL WINGS--
--BUT WEALTH HAD NOTHING TO DO WITH THAT. YOU SEE, WARREN IS ALSO THE MUTANT KNOWN AS THE AVENGING ANGEL!
PHONE CALL, MR. WORTHINGTON!
WHY, THANK YOU, MS. SOUTHERN!
--SPOKESMEN FOR THIS SPECIAL GOVERNMENT AGENCY...

WARREN? YEAH, IT'S BOBBY. YEP, I'M STILL IN L.A.
REASON I'M CALLING IS... WELL, YOU ONCE SAID THE SUMMER PLACE WAS ALWAYS OPEN, AND...

SOOO! FOUND YOURSELF A LADY, eh? SURE, COME ON UP! CANDY AND I'D LOVE TO HAVE YOU.

"YEAH, CANDY SOUTHERN! WE RAN INTO EACH OTHER IN SOCORRO--

--AND DECIDED TO ...AH, RENEW OUR FRIEND-SHIP.

SO FUEL UP THE OL' CHAMPS FLITTER AND COME JOIN US!
WILL DO, WARREN! SEE YOU TOMORROW... ABOUT TEN! AND THANKS!

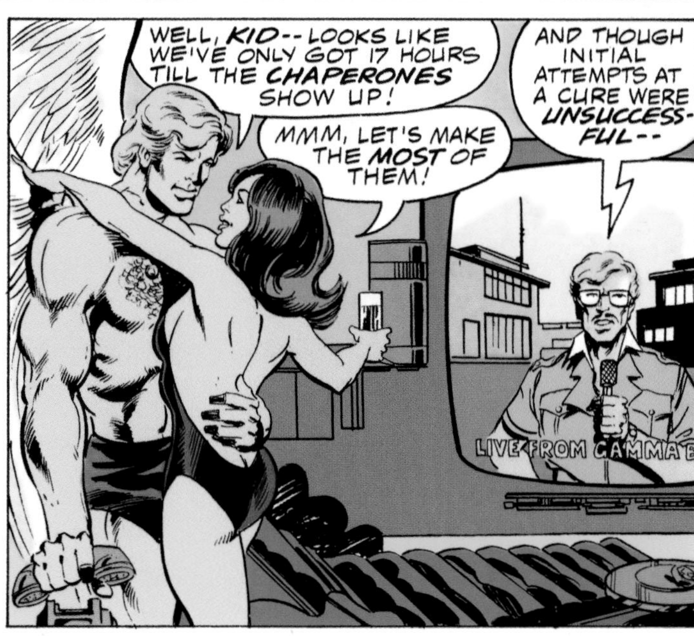
WELL, KID-- LOOKS LIKE WE'VE ONLY GOT 17 HOURS TILL THE CHAPERONES SHOW UP!
MMM, LET'S MAKE THE MOST OF THEM!
AND THOUGH INITIAL ATTEMPTS AT A CURE WERE UNSUCCESS-FUL--

--THE HOPE REMAINS THAT THIS TIME THE NATION'S HULK PROBLEM MAY AT LAST BE RESOLVED!
CHARLES P. IRWIN... CBS NEWS... AT GAMMA BASE.

A FINE REPORT, IRWIN. I'VE RARELY SEEN THE MEDIA TREAT GAMMA BASE SO FAIRLY.
WE DO OUR BEST, DOCTOR SAMSON.
TELL ME, WHAT ARE MY CHANCES OF INTER-VIEWING THE HULK?
WHAT?!

DO YOU KNOW WHAT YOU'RE ASKING? THE HULK IS LIKE A BOMB WAITING TO GO OFF! THE SLIGHTEST ANGER... ANXIETY... YOU NAME IT, AND WE'VE GOT A RAGING MONSTER ON OUR HANDS!
LOOK, DOC, I'VE COVERED 'NAM AND ANGOLA! I DON'T SCARE!

KA-PLANG
WHAT THE DEVIL?!
YOU WERE SAYING, MR. IRWIN?

HULK IS TIRED OF THIS PLACE!
HULK WANTS OUT... NOW!

I WAS AFRAID OF THIS. HE'S GOTTEN SLIGHTLY CLAUSTROPHOBIC, AND HE'S REACTED IN THE MOST DIRECT MANNER!
GET OUT OF HULK'S WAY!
MY GOD... I NEVER REALIZED HE WAS SO... BIG!

WHOOP!
SORRY, MR. IRWIN, BUT YOU'LL BE SAFER UP THERE!

NOW... I KNOW YOU'RE UPSET, HULK. BUT WE ALL WANT TO HELP... SO WHY DON'T YOU--?
SAMSON--

--YOU TALK TOO MUCH!

HULK STILL HASN'T FORGOTTEN HOW YOU TRICKED HULK... CALLED HULK STUPID!*
YEAH, WELL, I WAS WRONG, HULK--AND I ADMIT IT! YOU ARE DEFINITELY NOT STUPID!
*HULK #225--BOB.

YES, BUT YOU STILL TALK TO HULK AS IF HULK WAS STUPID!
URK

AND HULK HATES THAT!

HULK! WHAT'RE YA DOIN' TO THE DOC?
IT'S OKAY, JIM... I'M FINE.
I THINK.

HEY, TAKE IT EASY, M'MAN! WE KNOW YOU'VE HAD SOME HARD TIMES, BUT WE CAN WORK IT OUT.
STILL FRIENDS?
STILL... FRIENDS, JIM!
BLESS YOU, JIM! HE'S CALM AGAIN. WE MAY HAVE A CHANCE OF "CURING" THE HULK YET!

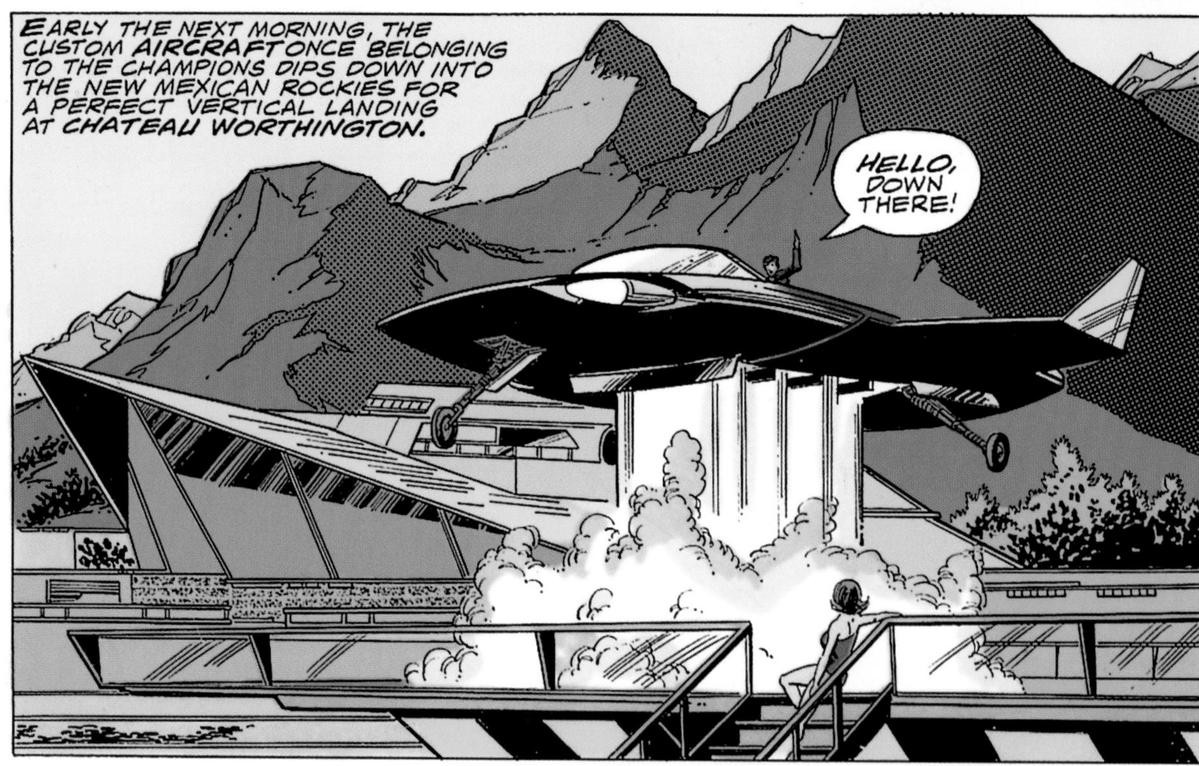

EARLY THE NEXT MORNING, THE CUSTOM AIRCRAFT ONCE BELONGING TO THE CHAMPIONS DIPS DOWN INTO THE NEW MEXICAN ROCKIES FOR A PERFECT VERTICAL LANDING AT CHATEAU WORTHINGTON.
HELLO, DOWN THERE!

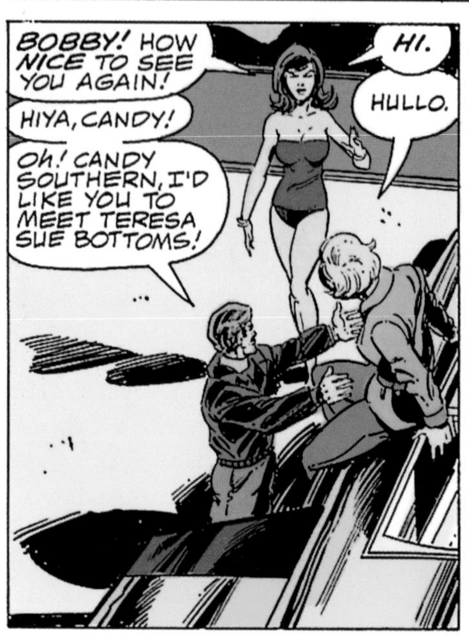

BOBBY! HOW NICE TO SEE YOU AGAIN!
HI.
HIYA, CANDY!
HULLO.
OH! CANDY SOUTHERN, I'D LIKE YOU TO MEET TERESA SUE BOTTOMS!

YOU CAN CALL ME... TERRI...
BOY, THIS IS REALLY SOME SPREAD, ISN'T IT, TERRI?
TERRI?

HI, I'M WARREN WORTHING-TON.
UH... UH... UH...

OH, MR. WORTHINGTON, I'VE READ SO MUCH ABOUT YOU, AND WHEN BOBBY TOLD ME THAT HE KNEW YOU, AND WE WERE COMING HERE, WHY, I WAS JUST SO EXCITED, YA KNOW?!
HEY... CALL ME WARREN, OKAY?
ENTHUSIASTIC, ISN'T SHE?
WHY DO I GET THE FEELING THIS ISN'T MY DAY?

AND WHILE THE FOURSOME GETS BETTER ACQUAINTED, HALFWAY UP A NEARBY PEAK A BUCKSKIN-CLAD FIGURE COMES OUT OF HIS CAVE AND STARTS DOWN THE MOUNTAIN TOWARDS...

POOLSIDE, SOME MINUTES LATER...
I HAVEN'T SEEN ANYONE GUSH LIKE THAT SINCE HIGH SCHOOL. I'M SURPRISED SHE HASN'T GONE IN AFTER WARREN.
AW, GIVE ME A BREAK, CANDY. SURE TERRI'S A LITTLE IMMATURE, BUT...

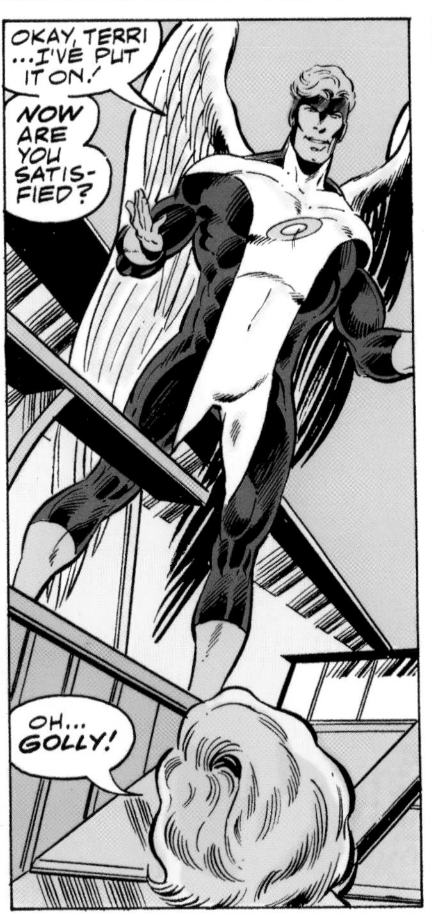

OKAY, TERRI ...I'VE PUT IT ON.!
NOW ARE YOU SATIS-FIED?
OH... GOLLY!

CAN YOU BELIEVE IT? SHE PUTS MORE FEELING INTO THAT "GOLLY" THAN SHE'S PUT INTO ANY-THING SHE'S EVER SAID TO ME!
HEY, IS SOMETHING WRONG CANDY? I MEAN, BESIDES...
I DON'T KNOW--

--BUT GRIZZLY ADAMS UP THERE DOESN'T LEAVE ME FEELING SAFE AND SECURE!
UH-OH! WARREN, I THINK WE'VE GOT TROUBLE!

TAKE IT EASY, PEOPLE. MAYBE THE MAN'S JUST LOST.
HELLO, SIR. IS THERE ANYTHING WE CAN DO FOR YOU?

YES, THERE IS.
YOU CAN SURRENDER-- OR DIE!
HOLY--!
BEEYOOOW

GIRLS, GET UPSTAIRS AND BOLT YOURSELVES IN!
NO WAY! IF YOU'RE IN DANGER, WE'RE STAYING!

ARE YOU OUT OF YOUR MIND? IF WE STAY HERE, WE'LL ONLY GET IN THE BOYS' WAY!
BUT I--!
COME ON!

HMMMM
BELIEVE ME, HON-- THE BOYS CAN HANDLE THIS!
ESPECIALLY IF BOBBY IS WHO I THINK HE IS.

BOBBY? I THOUGHT--!
SECRET IDENTITIES BE HANGED, WARREN! YOU COULD USE THE ICEMAN!
DO YOU THINK THIS WILL STOP ME, DRAKE?

IF YOU DO, YOU ARE SADLY MISTAKEN!

NOW ACCEPT YOUR FATE... SURRENDER, MUTANTS!

FORGET IT, MISTER! YOU JUST TIPPED YOUR HAND WITH THAT LITTLE TRICK!
YOU'RE NOT QUITE HUMAN YOUR-SELF!
KER
RACK!

AND THAT MEANS THE GLOVES ARE OFF!
KLANG

HOO-HA! SOUNDS LIKE BUFFALO BILL IS WEARING SOME SORT OF BODY ARMOR!
POOSH

A THING LIKE THAT COULD MAKE A FELLA SINK!
AND WE CAN'T LET THAT HAPPEN NOW CAN WE?

THERE! I DON'T THINK MR. TRESPASSER WILL BE MELTING OUT OF THAT FOR A WHILE!
NOT BAD--EH, WARREN?
NOT BAD AT ALL!

NOW, WHY DON'T YOU LET THE GIRLS OUT WHILE I CALL THE LOCAL GENDARMES?
OKAY BY ME, BOSSMAN! WHO KNOWS--

--MAYBE TERRI GETS OFF ON ICE, TOO!
HEY, DID YOU HEAR SOME-THING?
KRACK

CHATHOOM
OH, NO! THE GUY'S ANOTHER CRUMMY SENTINEL! WE CAN FIGHT SENTINELS IN OUR SLEEP!
WHEN WILL THEY EVER LEARN?
Uh... ANGEL?
SOMETHING TELLS ME THIS ISN'T AN ORDINARY SENTINEL.*
VERY ASTUTE, ICEMAN!
*THE MUTANT-HUNTING SENTINELS FIRST APPEARED IN X-MEN #14... REMEMBER? -- BOB.

FOR I AM THE
MASTER MOLD--
SENTINEL SUPREME!
AND IT IS MY SACRED DESTINY TO RID THE EARTH OF ALL MUTANTS!

BOBBY! I NEED A DELAYING ACTION--FAST!
GOTCHA, CHIEF!
NEVER TRIED THIS OUTSIDE OF THE OLD DANGER ROOM, BUT...

...WELL, HERE GOES NOTHING!
EH? IMPRESSIVE, DRAKE! YOU'RE ACTUALLY ABSORBING THE HEAT OUT OF THE VERY AIR-- LIKE A SUPER HEAT-PUMP!
IT'S A PITY YOUR ABSORPTION--

"--LEAVES YOU VULNERABLE TO MY FRIGI-BLAST!"
AAAKKK

HOW IRONIC! THE ICEMAN-- FELLED BY THE COLD!

SO SHALL ALL THE MUTANTS OF THE WORLD FALL!
FIRST, THE ICEMAN--

--AND NEXT, THE-- EH?
TRYING TO ESCAPE WON'T HELP YOU, ANGEL!
THERE IS NOWHERE ON THE FACE OF THIS PLANET YOU CAN HIDE FROM ME!
THE ROCKIES ECHO WITH THE ROAR OF MASTER MOLD'S BOOT-JETS--
--AS A SET OF STEEL SHUTTERS ARE CAUTIOUSLY OPENED, AND...
OMIGOD! A SENTINEL! IT MUST HAVE GRABBED BOBBY-- AND NOW IT'S AFTER WARREN!
GEE, I CAN SEE WHY HE'D GO AFTER WAR-REN, BUT WHY WOULD ANYBODY WANT BOBBY?
I HATED TO BREAK AND RUN, BUT THIS NEW MASTER MOLD MIGHT NOT HAVE THE USUAL SENTINEL SCRUPLES AGAINST HARMING NORMAL HUMANS!
I HAD TO LURE HIM AWAY FROM THE GIRLS!
NOW TO SEE IF I CAN SAVE MY OWN TAIL FEATHERS!

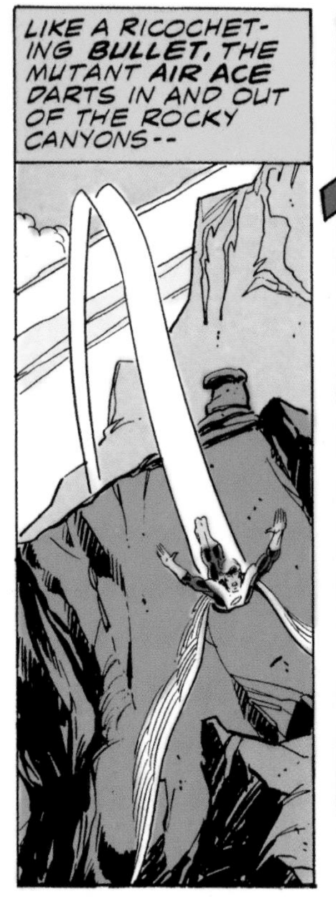
LIKE A RICOCHETING BULLET, THE MUTANT AIR ACE DARTS IN AND OUT OF THE ROCKY CANYONS--

--BUT TO NO AVAIL.
THA-BOOM
OH, NO! THIS THING'S LIKE IRON MAN AND THE HULK WRAPPED UP IN--!

THE HULK! OF COURSE!
GAMMA BASE IS ONLY A HUNDRED MILES DOWN RANGE!

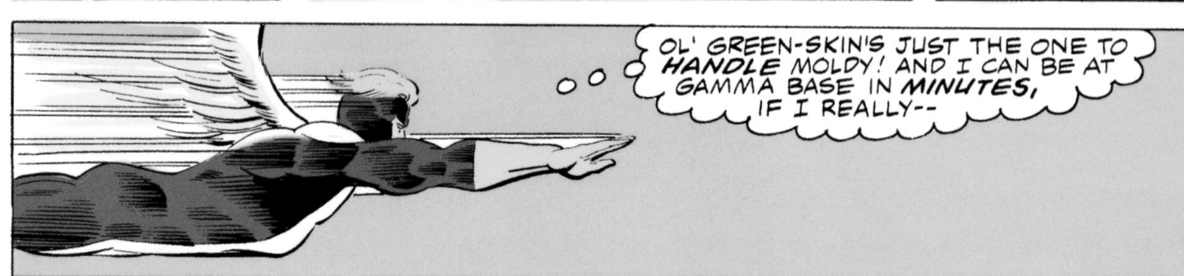
OL' GREEN-SKIN'S JUST THE ONE TO HANDLE MOLDY! AND I CAN BE AT GAMMA BASE IN MINUTES, IF I REALLY--

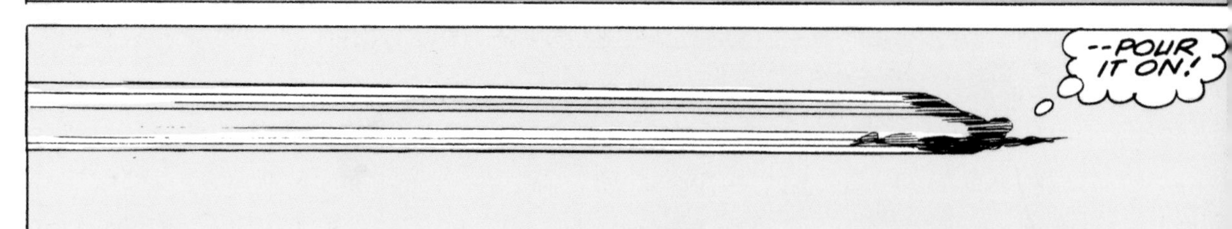
--POUR IT ON!

AND, AT GAMMA AIR CONTROL...
RADAR DUTY! OF ALL THE BUM ASSIGNMENTS! THERE'S NEVER ANY EXCITEMENT...
BLIP
BLIP

HEY, WHAT'S THAT ON THE SCREEN? TOO SMALL FOR A PLANE, TOO FAST FOR A BIRD--AND IT'S BEING FOLLOWED BY--!
BLIP
BLIP

BLIP

IT TAKES ONLY A SECOND FOR THE STARTLED RADIO OFFICER TO PUSH THE PANIC BUTTON--
--AND LESS THAN ONE MINUTE LATER, TWO SLEEK AIR FORCE JETS SCRAMBLE TO INTERCEPT THE STRANGE UFO'S.

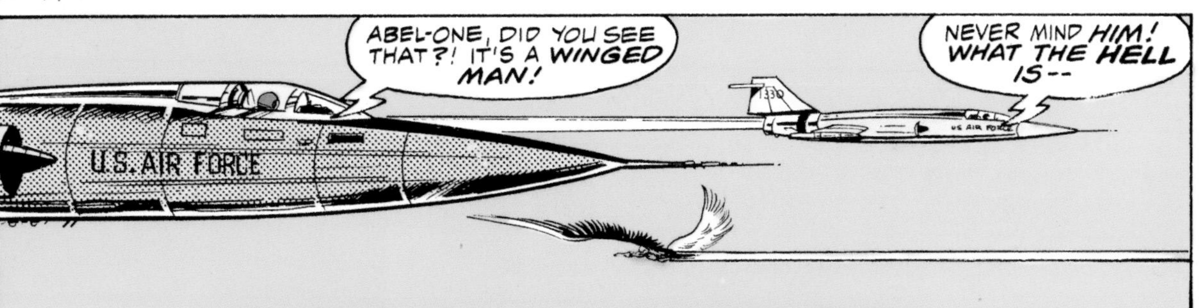
ABEL-ONE, DID YOU SEE THAT?! IT'S A WINGED MAN!
NEVER MIND HIM! WHAT THE HELL IS--
U.S. AIR FORCE

--THAT?!
VROOM
ABEL-TWO TO BASE! ABEL-TWO TO BASE--!

AAOOGAH
AAOOGAH

WHO AUTHORIZED THE USE OF THOSE KLAXONS? I ORDERED SILENCE! YOU WANT TO WAKE THE HULK?!
DOC... LOOK!

I... HUNH... MADE... HUNH ... IT.
THE ANGEL, ISN'T IT?
LORD ALMIGHTY, MAN, YOU LOOK AWFUL! WHAT'S WRONG?!

HE'S... HUNH... COMING!
WHO'S COMING? TAKE YOUR TIME, SON!
NO... HUNH ...TIME.

VOOM
GET AWAY FROM HIM!

IT IS NOT MY PURPOSE TO HARM ANY HUMANS! ALL I WANT IS THE MUTANT!
WHAT?!

IF YOU THINK YOU CAN JUST FLY IN HERE AND GRAB SOMEBODY, THEN YOU CAN THINK--

KLATHOOM
WHAT IS ALL THIS NOISE?
--AGAIN.

STAY OUT OF THIS, LITTLE MAN! IT DOES NOT CONCERN YOU!
MAN?! HULK IS NO LITTLE MAN! HULK IS THE HULK!
AND NO BIG ROBOT TELLS HULK WHAT TO DO!
OH, NO?
KROOM
WHAT IS THIS?! FIRST, ROBOT SMASHES HULK'S FRIEND--
--THEN, ROBOT TRIES TO SMASH HULK! AND NOW--
--HULK IS WET AGAIN!

NO ONE DOES THAT TO HULK!
HULK... WAIT!

THAT'S NO ORDINARY ROBOT.
THAT'S A SENTI-NEL!

LIKE TWIN HUMAN CANNON-BALLS, THE GAMMA-POWERED TITANS SOAR INTO THE SKY AFTER THEIR QUARRY.
THE HULK CATCHES HOLD OF MASTER MOLD'S RIGHT BOOT, SINKING HIS MIGHTY FINGERS DEEP INTO THE METAL.

DOC SAMSON IS NOT SO LUCKY.

THE PSYCHIATRIST/STRONGMAN PLUMMETS BACK TO EARTH... LANDING FINALLY WITH A SICKENING...
THUD

FASTER, JULIUS! HE LANDED JUST AHEAD!
BUT, GENERAL ROSS... SIR, YOU SHOULDN'T EXCITE YOURSELF! YOU WERE JUST RELEASED FROM THE HOSPITAL--*
--AND YOUR RIBS HAVEN'T FULLY HEALED!
*WHERE HE WAS RECUPER-ATING FROM A BLOW FROM THE HULK. SEE HULK #226--BOB.
HANG MY RIBS! SAMSON, ARE YOU ALL RIGHT?
I... THINK SO, SIR!

SAMSON, I... THAT IS... FIRST WINGED MEN, THEN, ROBOTS, AND NOW...
...NOW WHAT?

WERE THE FLUSTERED GENERAL ROSS TO GAZE UPWARD, HE MIGHT CATCH ONE GLIMPSE OF THE ANSWER HE SEEKS.
THIS STUPID ROBOT FLIES FAST! HE TRIES TO BLOW THE HULK OFF WITH WIND!

BUT IT WON'T WORK, ROBOT! THE HULK IS TOO STRONG FOR YOU!

INCREDIBLE! THE BRUTE MUST POSSESS ALMOST UNLIMITED STAMINA.
GIVEN TIME, HE MIGHT ACTUALLY DO ME HARM --BUT IN JUST A MOMENT, HIS POWER WILL BE ALL FOR NAUGHT!

DO YOU HEAR HULK, ROBOT? DO... YOU...
...WHAT?
WHY CAN'T HULK SPEAK? WHY...

HIS QUESTION FADES AWAY, AS THE LAST ATOMS OF OXYGEN IN THE MAN-MONSTER'S LUNGS ARE EXHAUSTED.
FOR NOT EVEN THE RAMPAGING HULK CAN BREATHE FREELY...
...IN SPACE!

THE MASTER MOLD ROCKETS ON THROUGH THE ICY-COLD VOID, SEEMINGLY OBLIVIOUS TO THE TINY GREEN LIFE FORM THAT IS CAUGHT IN HIS BOOT.
HE DRAWS EVER NEARER THE JAGGED BULK OF A SMALL ASTEROID, SWINGING ABOUT IN THE EARTH'S GRAVITY WELL...
...AN ASTEROID WHICH, ON CLOSER OBSERVATION, IS MORE THAN A MERE CHUNK OF ROCK.

SLOWLY...
...LIKE SWIMMING THROUGH DARK MOLASSES...

...WARREN WORTHINGTON FIGHTS HIS WAY BACK TO CONSCIOUSNESS.

LOOK OUT! THE MASTER MOLD--!

WHERE ARE WE? WHO... WHAT ARE YOU REALLY? AND WHY...?
TOO LATE, MUTANT! YOU AND YOUR ONCE-FROZEN ALLY HAVE FOUND YOUR FINAL HOMES.
ANGEL
BLOB
MA
SO MANY QUESTIONS, ANGEL? I MIGHT ANSWER, WERE IT NOT SO SATISFYING TO KEEP YOU IN THE DARK!
HA HA HA
PINCH ME, SOMEBODY! UNLESS I'M ASLEEP--
--I'M HEARING A SENTINEL LAUGH!
UNH
YOU'RE AWAKE, BOBBY.
AND SO IS OUR BIG GREEN BUDDY!

WHAT IS HULK DOING IN THIS STUPID TUBE?
BLOB

THE TUBE IS FORMED OF TEMPERED PLASTEEL, SPECIALLY DESIGNED TO RESTRAIN THE AWESOME POWER OF THE MUTANT CALLED BLOB.
LET HULK OUT!
BLOB
AS FAR AS THE HULK IS CONCERNED, IT MIGHT AS WELL BE PAPIER MÂCHÉ!

WARREN! LET ME OUT!
CONSIDER IT DONE, BOB!
WHERE IS THE ROBOT?

THE ROBOT MUST HAVE PUT HULK IN THE TUBE! HE THOUGHT HE'D TRAP THE HULK!
COME ON OUT, FROSTY, AND JOIN THE PARTY!
FREED FROM THE DAMPING EFFECT OF THE TUBE, BOB DRAKE'S UNIQUE POWERS SPRING TO LIFE--

--WHILE THE HULK APPLIES HIS SOMEWHAT LESS SUBTLE POWER TO THE CHAMBER'S DOOR.

WOW! HOW CAN ANYTHING MORTAL BE THAT STRONG?
BEATS ME, FEATHERS! FROM WHAT PROFESSOR X TOLD ME, HE EVEN GAVE THE JUGGERNAUT A RUN FOR HIS MONEY ONCE!*
*HULK #172--BOB.

THE DOOR IS NEARLY A METER THICK, BUILT OF INTERTWINING BANDS OF THE HARDEST FORGED STEEL. IT FALLS IN LESS THAN 30 SECONDS.
ROBOT! HULK IS COMING FOR YOU!
BUT THE ROBOT IS NOT IN THE OBSERVATION CHAMBER. THE ONLY THING THERE...

--IS A VERY GOOD VIEW.
SPACE?!
OH, CRUD! WE'RE IN ORBIT! HOW DO WE GET DOWN TO EARTH FROM HERE?
HUNH! HULK HAS FALLEN FURTHER THAN THAT! HULK CAN GET DOWN EASILY!
BUT FIRST, HULK MUST SMASH THAT ROBOT!

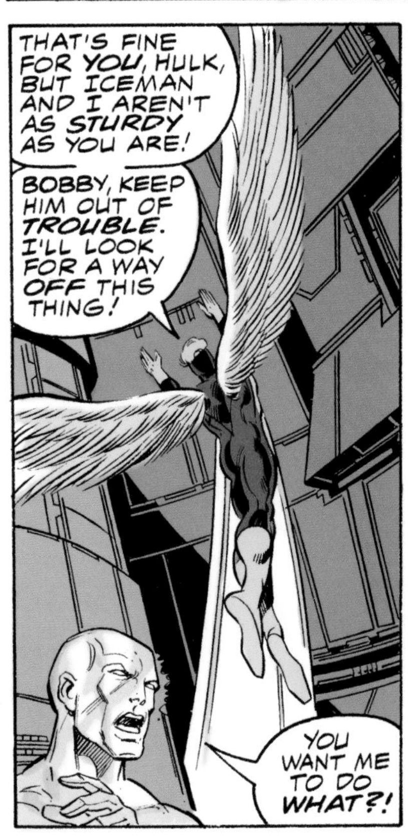
THAT'S FINE FOR YOU, HULK, BUT ICEMAN AND I AREN'T AS STURDY AS YOU ARE!
BOBBY, KEEP HIM OUT OF TROUBLE. I'LL LOOK FOR A WAY OFF THIS THING!
YOU WANT ME TO DO WHAT?!

HEY... Uh, HULK, OLD BUDDY... WHAT DO YOU SAY WE HANG OUT HERE UNTIL ANGEL GETS BACK?
HULK?
BAH!

I WAS AFRAID YOU'D SAY THAT!
Oh, WELL! WAIT FOR ME, MR. GREEN!

THE TECHNOLOGY IN THIS PLACE IS UNBELIEVABLE! THAT, UNLESS I MISS MY GUESS, IS THE POWER CORE FOR A FUSION REACTOR!
IF THIS NEW MASTER MOLD HAS LICKED THE PROBLEMS ON A BABY LIKE THAT, I HATE TO THINK WHAT ELSE HE HAS UP HIS METAL SLEEVES!
MEANWHILE, IN ANOTHER SECTION...
COME ON, HULK, YOU'LL NEVER SNEAK UP ON MOLDY THAT WAY!
THE HULK DOESN'T SNEAK! THE HULK SMASHES!
WELL... SURE. BUT SOME OF THESE DOORS MAY BE UNLOCKED AND...
HOLY SMOKE!
I WONDERED WHY THIS PLACE SEEMED SO BIG.
"IT'S BUILT TO SCALE FOR MASTER MOLD!"
England
28
32·5
U. S. A.
77
FOREIGN
10
PTO
AND FROM THE LOOKS OF THAT SCREEN, HE'S GOT A KING-SIZED VERSION OF CEREBRO* AT WORK!
ROBOT!
SHH! KEEP IT DOWN, HULK!
*PROFESSOR XAVIER'S MUTANT-TRACKING COMPUTER-- BOB.

HE'LL HEAR--! HEY!
GET YOUR COLD HANDS OFF HULK, LITTLE MAN!
HULK TOLD YOU, HE DOESN'T CARE IF THE ROBOT HEARS HIM!

AND HULK DOESN'T NEED YOUR HELP TO FIGHT!

WHAT? WHO DARES TO ATTACK THE MASTER MOLD?
KRASH
THE HULK DARES, ROBOT!

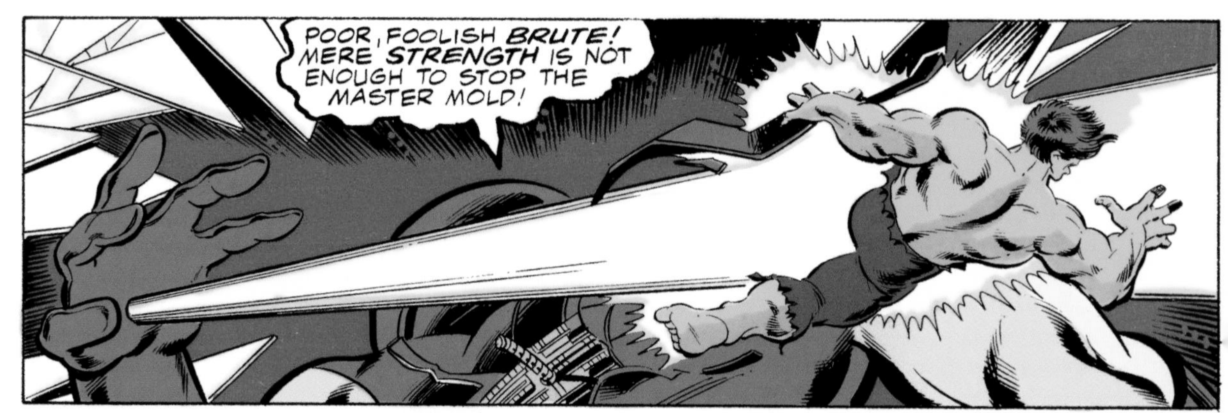
POOR, FOOLISH BRUTE! MERE STRENGTH IS NOT ENOUGH TO STOP THE MASTER MOLD!

NOT WHEN MY CONCUSSION BLAST CAN BLOW YOU AWAY, LIKE A THISTLE IN THE WIND.

HULK IS NO THISTLE.

AND A ROBOT CANNOT FIGHT... IF HE CANNOT STAND!!

NOW, ROBOT--YOU WILL LEARN THAT NOTHING IS STRONGER THAN THE HULK!

NOTHING!
ZZZAAPP
YOU HAVE TRIED MY PATIENCE WITH YOUR TALK OF STRENGTH, MONSTER! IT WILL DO YOU LITTLE GOOD AGAINST A MILLION VOLTS OF UNBRIDLED ENERGY!
REMARKABLE! I BELIEVE THAT HE IS STILL BREATHING!

ALL RIGHT, WHAT'S GOING ON HERE? REAL SENTINELS DON'T LAUGH OR SHOW SURPRISE!
JUST WHAT THE DEVIL ARE YOU?

OH, I AM INDEED A SENTINEL NOW, DRAKE... THOUGH I WAS NOT ALWAYS SO.
BEFORE I DIED, I WAS A MAN... A MAN NAMED STEVEN LANG.

"I WAS THE HEAD OF PROJECT ARMAGEDDON, A GOVERNMENT STUDY OF MUTANTS--AND I WAS DEDICATED TO THEIR EXTERMINATION.
"AT LEAST, I WAS BEFORE I MET DEATH AT THE HANDS OF THE ACCURSED X-MEN!*
*X-MEN #100 --BOB.

"BUT THE CRASH OF MY FLYING GUNSHIP DID NOT KILL ME IMMEDIATELY. AS THE COWARDLY X-MEN FLED MY BURNING SHIELD SPACE PLATFORM--
"--I PULLED MYSELF FROM THE WRECKAGE AND CRAWLED TO THE CHAMBER WHICH HELD MY GREATEST WEAPON--

"--THE MASTER MOLD!
"IF I WAS TO DIE, ALL MUTANTKIND WOULD SUFFER FOR IT!

"BUT, AS WITH MY OTHER SENTINELS, THE MASTER MOLD'S CIRCUITRY DEVIATED TOO MUCH FROM BOLIVAR TRASK'S* ORIGINAL DESIGNS.
"I DID NOT MERELY ACTIVATE THE MASTER MOLD.
"AS I BREATHED MY LAST, I BECAME THE MASTER MOLD!
*TRASK BUILT THE FIRST SENTINELS. SEE X-MEN #14 --BOB.

BALONEY!
Eh?

WHEN THE SHIELD BOYS RECLAIMED THEIR ORBITAL PLATFORM, THEY FOUND LANG.
HE'S STILL ALIVE IN A GOVERNMENT HOSPITAL--A MINDLESS VEGETABLE!
WHATEVER YOU MAY BE, YOU'RE NOT STEVEN LANG!
THAT... CANNOT BE!
MY MIND... MY MEMORIES ARE LANG'S! I MUST BE HIM! I MUST!
THE HULK DOESN'T CARE WHO YOU ARE, ROBOT!
THAKOOM
HULK WILL SMASH YOU JUST THE SAME!

BAM

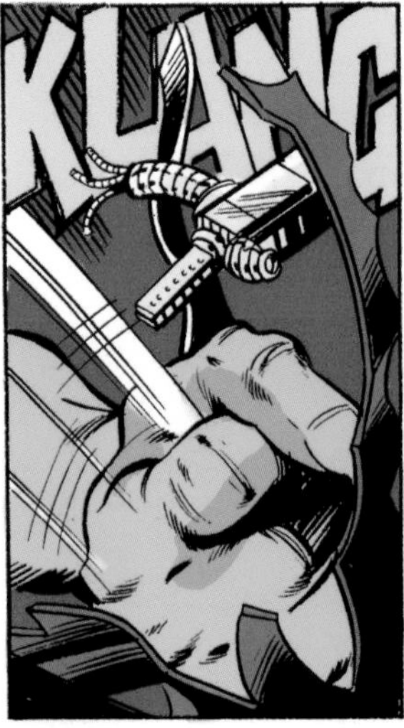
KLANG

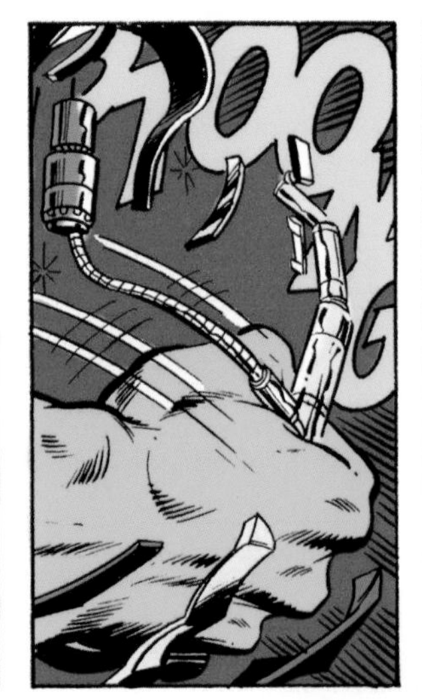
ZOOOONG

KOOM

I... THINK I'M GOING TO BE SICK.
UH... YEAH, HULK, ARE YOU READY TO GO NOW? PLEASE?

BAH! HULK MIGHT AS WELL GO. ROBOT WILL NOT BOTHER HULK AGAIN.

THE MOTLEY TRIO LEAVES THE COMMAND CHAMBER--

--BUT BEHIND THEM THE HAND OF MASTER MOLD TWITCHES SPAS-MODICALLY TO LIFE!

THERE'S OUR RIDE HOME, FOLKS!
A LITTLE ON THE SMALL SIDE, ISN'T IT?

IT'LL BE A TIGHT SQUEEZE, BUT I THINK WE'LL FIT.
YEAH, I GUESS. COME ON, HULK, IT'LL BE FUN--
--JUST LIKE STAR WARS!

BUT BEFORE THE HULK CAN ENTER THE TINY CRAFT...
MUTANTS! ESCAPE IS IMPOSSIBLE! I HAVE JAMMED ALL EMERGENCY CAPSULES!
IF I AM TO DIE A ROBOT, YOU SHALL DIE, TOO. I... HAVE SET THE FUSION REACTOR TO OVERLOAD.
ROBOT!

HULK, WHERE ARE YOU GOING? WE'VE GOT TO GET OUT OF HERE! I'M SURE WE CAN UNJAM--!
NO! HULK IS NOT GOING ANYWHERE UNTIL THE ROBOT IS SMASHED!

OH, YEAH?!
HUNH?!

I HOPE YOU KNOW WHAT YOU'RE DOING, BOBBY!
COME AND GET ME, YA BIG GREEN GOOF!
NYAH, NYAH!

YOU WANT TO TRICK HULK INTO THAT LITTLE ROOM, BUT IT WON'T WORK!
YOU WANT TO GO?

THEN GO!
WITH AS LITTLE EFFORT AS A MAN KICKING A TIRE, THE EMERALD MAN-MONSTER KICKS THE ESCAPE CAPSULE FREE--
--AIRLOCK AND ALL!

AIR RUSHES AWAY FROM HULK-- PULLING AT HULK!
HULK MUST HOLD BREATH!

ALMOST BEFORE HE CAN REACT, THE HULK IS SUCKED OUT INTO THE VOID. HE HALTS HIMSELF ON THE VERY LIP OF THE OPENING...

...AND DOGGEDLY FIGHTS HIS WAY BACK IN!
HULK WILL SMASH THAT ROBOT FOR GOOD!

MEANWHILE, PROPELLED BY THE HULK'S KICK, THE ESCAPE MODULE TUMBLES STEADILY TOWARD THE GREEN HILLS OF EARTH--
--AT AN EVER-INCREASING SPEED.

AND AS THE FALLING BODY MEETS THE OUTER FRINGES OF ATMOSPHERE--
--THINGS START TO GET VERY HOT.

WARREN... I HOPE THE BRAKING ROCKETS KICK IN PRETTY SOON...
...'CAUSE IF THEY DON'T--!
I KNOW... WE WON'T HAVE TO WORRY ABOUT A ROUGH LANDING.

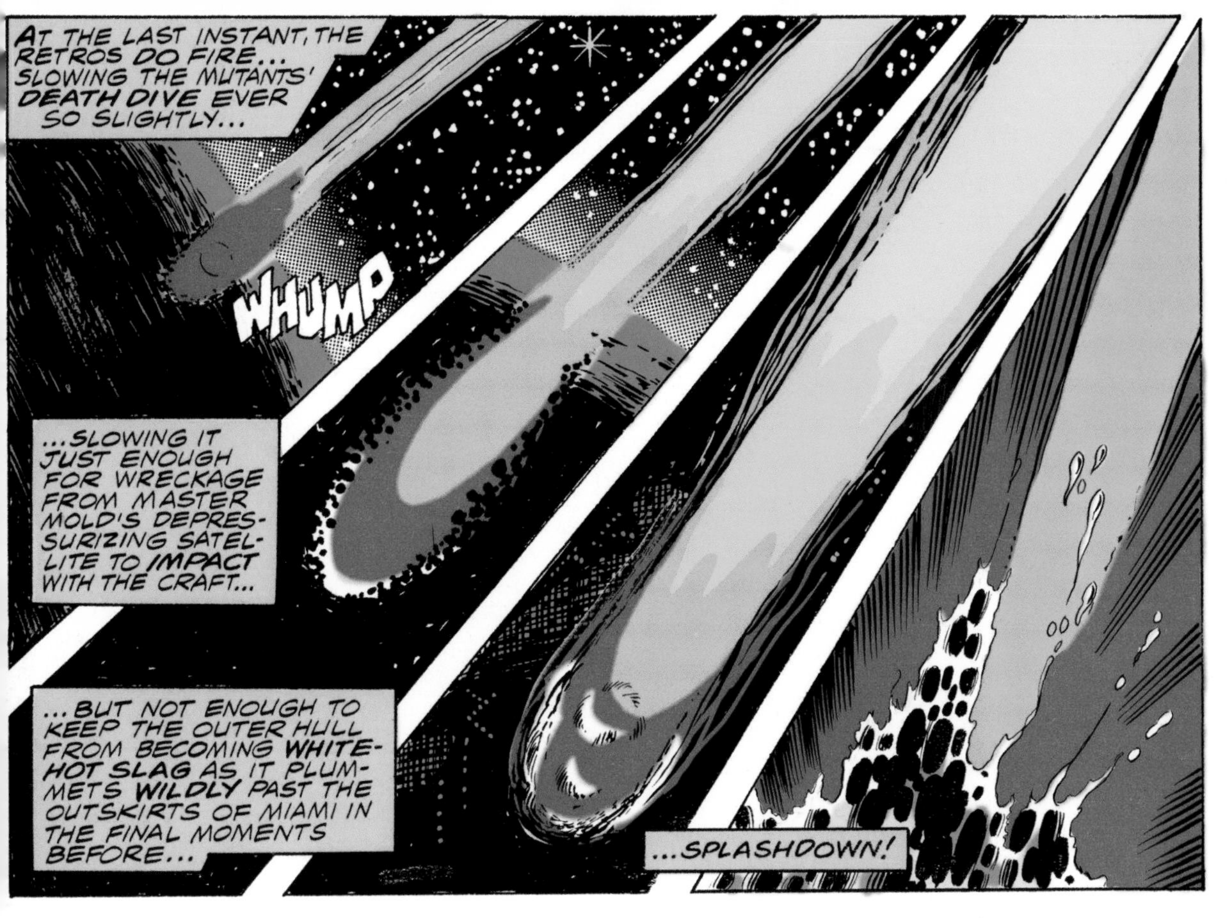
AT THE LAST INSTANT, THE RETROS DO FIRE... SLOWING THE MUTANTS' DEATH DIVE EVER SO SLIGHTLY...
WHUMP
...SLOWING IT JUST ENOUGH FOR WRECKAGE FROM MASTER MOLD'S DEPRESSURIZING SATELLITE TO IMPACT WITH THE CRAFT...
...BUT NOT ENOUGH TO KEEP THE OUTER HULL FROM BECOMING WHITE-HOT SLAG AS IT PLUMMETS WILDLY PAST THE OUTSKIRTS OF MIAMI IN THE FINAL MOMENTS BEFORE...
...SPLASHDOWN!

SUDDENLY, A SMALL AREA OF THE ATLANTIC OCEAN IS SEIZED BY A VIOLENT BUT HIGHLY LOCALIZED STORM OF BOILING RAIN--
--AS IF THE PLANET WERE BIDDING ONE LAST SALUTE TO THE FALLEN ANGEL AND HIS FRIEND.

BUT THEN, LIKE A CORK IN A FISH TANK, THE CAPSULE BOBS TO THE SURFACE, ROLLING UNEASILY IN THE ANGRY SEA...

POONT

EASY DOES IT, BOB! WE'RE HOME FREE NOW!
NO... NOT YET! THIS THING WON'T STAY AFLOAT LONG!
GOTTA ICE US A RAFT... SOMETHING!

CAREFUL, MAN! THAT RE-ENTRY TOOK A LOT OUT OF YOU. WE'RE SAFE... TRUST ME!
YEAH... BUT WHAT ABOUT THE HULK?

AS IF IN ANSWER TO ICEMAN'S QUESTION, THE HEAVENS SUDDENLY ERUPT WITH THE LIGHT OF A MINIATURE STAR--
...AS THE MASTER MOLD'S PLANETOID... CEASES TO EXIST.
THE HULK. OH, MY GOD.
HE WAS STILL UP THERE.

THERE'S NO WAY EVEN HE COULD HAVE SURVIVED THAT BLAST.
I HOPE HE AT LEAST GOT A FEW MORE LICKS IN ON MASTER MOLD BEFORE... THE END.

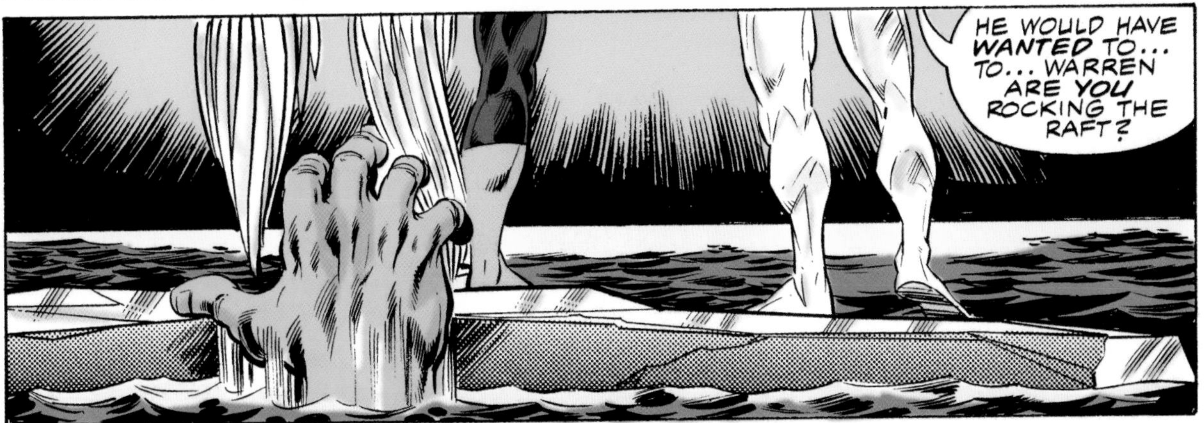
HE WOULD HAVE WANTED TO... TO... WARREN ARE YOU ROCKING THE RAFT?

WHY DON'T YOU HELP HULK OUT OF THE WATER?
HULK? BUT HOW?
BAH! STUPID FLOOR CAME LOOSE IN HULK'S HANDS, AND HULK FELL.

SO THAT'S WHAT HIT THE CAPSULE! YOU GRABBED ON TO THE UNDERSIDE!
UH... YEAH. BUT YOU HAVE TO BE GETTING BACK TO THE DES-ERT... RIGHT, HULK? YOU PROMISED YOUR FRIENDS, DIDN'T YOU?
WE'RE GLAD YOU MADE IT, GREEN GUY!
FRIENDS?
AT GAMMA BASE, HULK. REMEMBER?

BASE... YES! JIM IS AT BASE! HULK MUST GO BACK--
--NOW!
HEY!
THOOM
WELL, THERE HE GOES! I DON'T KNOW WHAT DOC SAMSON HAS PLANNED FOR HIM,* BUT I HOPE IT WORKS!
YEAH, HE REALLY DESERVES HIS PLACE IN THE SUN.
*SEE HULK #228 TO FIND OUT --BOB.

SPEAKING OF PLACES IN THE SUN, WE'D BETTER HUSTLE BACK TO THE MOUNTAINS OURSELVES.
WE STILL HAVE TO FIND OUT IF TERRI SUE GETS OFF ON ICE. THAT IS, IF CANDY HASN'T KILLED HER BY NOW!
WHY ME, LORD? WHY ME?
END

HULK: RAGING THUNDER #1

HULK

A MONSTER
WHOSE RAGE FUELS
HIS MAGNIFICENT
STRENGTH.

UNBEATABLE

JEFF PARKER – **WRITING**
MITCH BREITWEISER – **DRAWING**
MOOSE BAUMANN – **COLORING**
BLAMBOT'S NATE PIEKOS – **LETTERING**
LAND & OBACK – **COVER**
PAUL ACERIOS – **PRODUCTION**
NATHAN COSBY – **ASSISTANT EDITOR**
MARK PANICCIA – **EDITOR**
JOE QUESADA – **EDITOR IN CHIEF**
DAN BUCKLEY – **PUBLISHER**

THUNDRA AT DAWN!

Originally presented in **FANTASTIC FOUR #133**
GERRY CONWAY – **SCRIPTER**
RAMONA FRADON – **PENCILER**
JOE SINNOTT – **INKER**
STAN GOLDBERG – **COLORIST**
JOHN COSTANZA – **LETTERER**
ROY THOMAS – **PLOTTER AND EDITOR**

A WARRIOR
FROM A FUTURE OF FEMALE
DOMINANCE.

THUNDRA

NORTH AMERICA. AREA FORMERLY KNOWN AS SOUTHERN UTAH.
THE PERIMETER IS CLOSED!
TWO CENTURIES AGO.
HISTORY TELLS US MEN WERE ALWAYS WARLIKE.
AT LEAST IN THE OLD DAYS, THEY FOUGHT OTHER MEN.

NOW RECOGNIZED AS WESTERN TERRITORY OF THE UNITED SISTERHOOD REPUBLIC.
OUR CAPTURES SPOKE TRUE! THE WOMEN DO HAVE A SECRET PROJECT IN THE ROCKLANDS.
UNLESS THE PROJECT IS A MASS GRAVE, IT IS DOOMED TO FAILURE!

THEY WERE MUCH WEAKER THEN, BUT THEY WERE MUCH LIKE THEIR DESCENDANTS.
THEY HATED THOSE WHO WERE DIFFERENT. FEARED THEM.
WHY DO YOU FOLLOW HULK? WHY?!

YOU COWARDS ARE NOT DEALING WITH A FACTION OF FARMERS LIKE YOU USUALLY ATTACK. TODAY YOU FACE THE ROYAL GUARD OF...
...THUNDRA!

PUT THEIR FORCES DOWN, SISTERS! WE MUST PROTECT THE POST AT ALL COSTS!
LEAVE NO MAN ALIVE!
WE WILL, MATRIARCH!
THE PEOPLE OF THE OLD DAYS WOULD BE ASTONISHED HOW MUCH HAD CHANGED IN TWO HUNDRED YEARS.

DEPLOYING THE HULKBUSTER CRUISE MISSLE... NOW.
COPY THAT. AREA CLEARED.
101
NOT THAT THE WORLD WAS DIVIDED INTO TWO MAIN FACTIONS AND CONSTANTLY AT WAR.
THAT WOULDN'T SURPRISE THEM.

OUR WINDOW FOR TIMELINE CROSSOVER IS IN THREE HOURS, THUNDRA.
I WILL BE READY.
BUT THE IDEA THAT MEN WOULD ONE DAY REJECT THEIR WIVES. MOTHERS. SISTERS. DAUGHTERS. FROM WHAT THE LEARNING CUBES TEACH US, THIS WOULD HAVE SHOCKED THEM.

THEY WOULD CALL THIS IMPOSSIBLE. IMPROBABLE, AT LEAST.
MILLIONS OF FUTURES COULD RESULT FROM THEIR POINT.
THIS WAS JUST ONE OF THEM.
TIMESCAPES ARE ALMOST ALIGNED, THUNDRA! THE NEXT WINDOW WON'T BE FOR MONTHS!
AN "EVENTUALITY." AN UNLIKELY ONE.

YET IT FELT REAL ENOUGH IN THIS CENTURY.
AVELA, IF I DON'T INTERCEDE, THEY...THEY COULD FALL!
RRRAAGHHH
THUNDRA, NO. WE CAN'T TAKE ANY RISKS--YOU HAVE TO BE READY FOR THE TIME JUMP!
COME BACK!
INCOMING!
DITCH! DITCH!
AAAGH!

GRAAAHHH!
MOVE! MOVE!

DO YOU HEAR HIM, THUNDRA? THE GREATEST MAN OF ALL IS COMING FOR YOU!

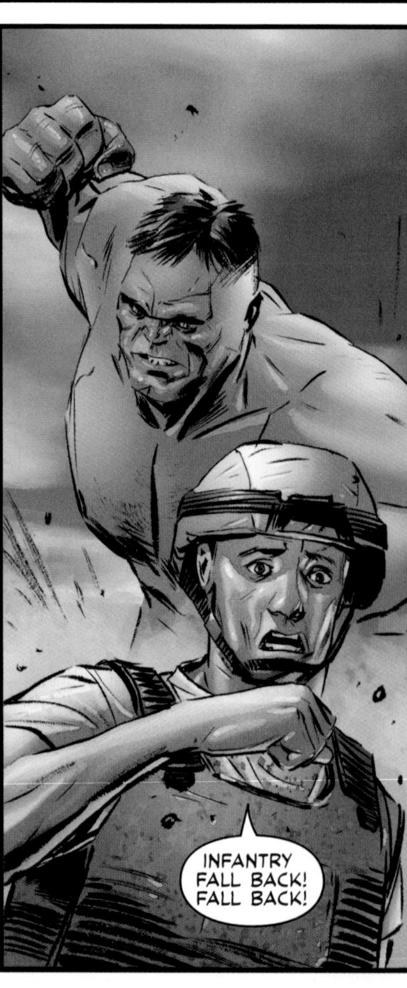
INFANTRY FALL BACK! FALL BACK!

HIS NAME IS DEATH!

BREAK OFF! DISENGAGE!

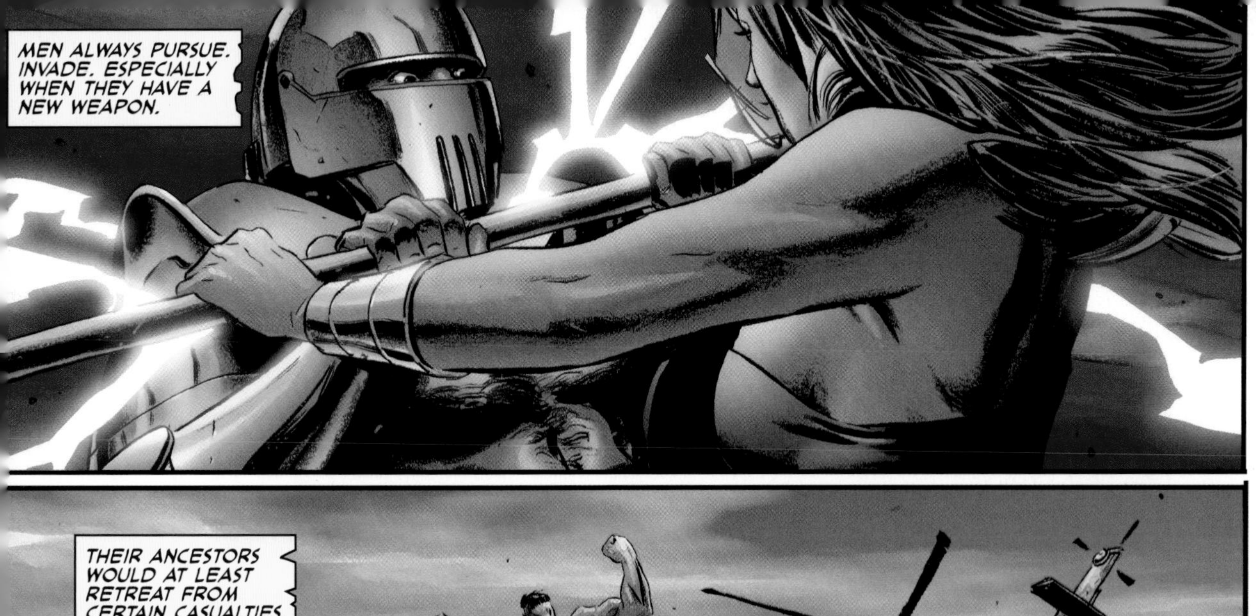
MEN ALWAYS PURSUE. INVADE. ESPECIALLY WHEN THEY HAVE A NEW WEAPON.

THEIR ANCESTORS WOULD AT LEAST RETREAT FROM CERTAIN CASUALTIES.

BUT NOT THIS TRIBE OF MEN.

EACH AGE HAD A SURVIVOR THOUGH, WHO WOULD NEVER GIVE IN.
BOTH STOOD VICTORIOUS IN THEIR ERAS.
YET IT WASN'T THE SAVAGE OF THE PAST WHO LEFT SO MANY DEAD IN HIS WAKE.

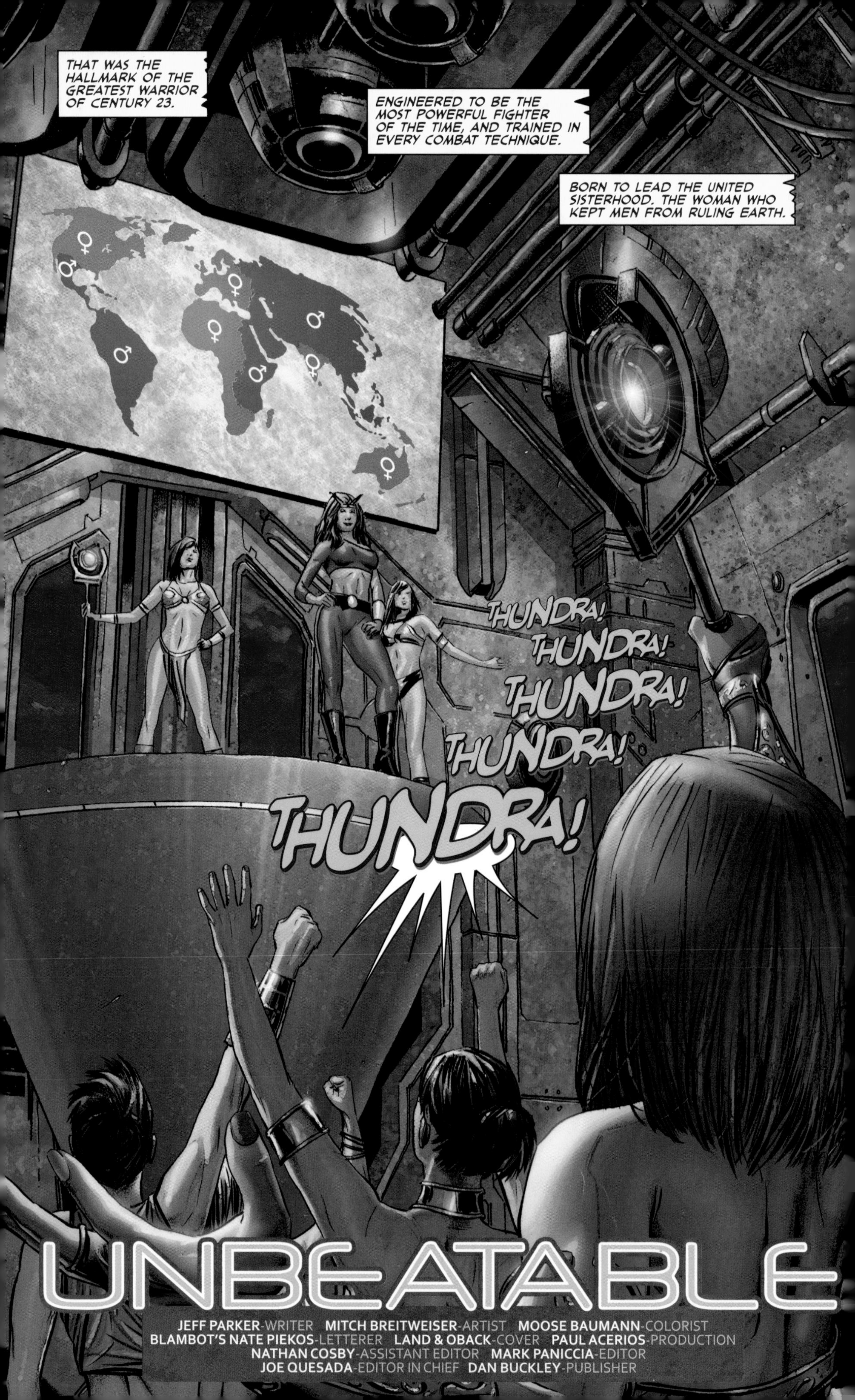
THAT WAS THE HALLMARK OF THE GREATEST WARRIOR OF CENTURY 23.
ENGINEERED TO BE THE MOST POWERFUL FIGHTER OF THE TIME, AND TRAINED IN EVERY COMBAT TECHNIQUE.
BORN TO LEAD THE UNITED SISTERHOOD. THE WOMAN WHO KEPT MEN FROM RULING EARTH.
THUNDRA!
THUNDRA!
THUNDRA!
THUNDRA!
THUNDRA!
UNBEATABLE
JEFF PARKER-WRITER MITCH BREITWEISER-ARTIST MOOSE BAUMANN-COLORIST
BLAMBOT'S NATE PIEKOS-LETTERER LAND & OBACK-COVER PAUL ACERIOS-PRODUCTION
NATHAN COSBY-ASSISTANT EDITOR MARK PANICCIA-EDITOR
JOE QUESADA-EDITOR IN CHIEF DAN BUCKLEY-PUBLISHER

HAIL OUR MATRIARCH WHO WILL ONCE AGAIN TEAR THROUGH TIME AND SPACE!
WILL YOU CHALLENGE ANOTHER LIKE THE MAN BEN GRIMM?

NO! OUR GOVERNESS WILL NOW CHALLENGE THE MOST POWERFUL MAN OF ALL TIME!
THE ONE BORN BRUCE BANNER, BUT FEARED THROUGHOUT HISTORY AS... THE HULK!

SEND THE WORD TO EVERY PROVINCE! TONIGHT THE LEGEND GOES DOWN!
THUN-DRA! THUN-DRA! THUN-DRA! THUN-DRA! THUN-DRA! THUN-DRA! THUN-DRA! THUN-DRA! THUN-DRA! THUN-DRA! THUN-DRA!

POLITICS.
YOU THINK ANY LEADER HOLDS A REPUBLIC TOGETHER WITHOUT LYING TO HER PEOPLE?

THESE ENCOUNTERS BOOST MORALE ALL THE WAY TO THE BORDERLANDS. THEY DO NOT NEED TO KNOW THE REAL PURPOSE.

IT'S TIME.
IT HAD BEEN YEARS SINCE THUNDRA FACED THE MIGHTY BEN GRIMM IN BATTLE. THE YOUNGEST GIRLS KNOW OF HOW SHE RISKED THE UNSTABLE CHRONO-GATE TO FACE THE LEGENDARY WARRIORS THAT THE MEN CELEBRATED--BUILDING HER OWN LEGEND.
IN TRUTH GRIMM BECAME AN ALLY, AND HIS TEAM CAME TO OUR TIME TO HELP US FIGHT ONE OF THE MALE WARLORDS.
THUN-DRA! THUN-DRA! THUN-DRA! THUN-DRA! THUN-DRA! THUN-DRA! THUN-DRA! THUN-DRA! THUN-DRA! THUN-DRA!
MANY DECEPTIONS WERE PUT INTO PLACE TO KEEP THE UNITED SISTERHOOD FROM KNOWING THAT MEN HAD HELPED OUR CAUSE.
SIMILAR DECEPTIONS CONVINCED THE FANTASTIC FOUR THAT OUR WARRING FACTIONS WERE BROUGHT TOGETHER, SO THEY COULD RETURN HOME.
AN ANSWER THAT MADE PERFECT SENSE TO PEOPLE FROM FAMILIES OF MEN AND WOMEN.
THEY COULDN'T KNOW HOW RIDICULOUS SUCH A THING WAS HERE. EVEN THOUGH THEIR WORLD IS WHERE OURS BEGAN.

IT WAS IN THIS TIME THAT MEN AND WOMEN WERE PUSHED APART BY THE SLIGHTEST THINGS...POLITICS, ART, BUSINESS, ENTERTAINMENT. EVERY PART OF THEIR SOCIETY BEGAN TO TREAT THEM AS IF THEY WERE IRREVOCABLY DIFFERENT. IN COMPETITION.
EVENTUALLY SCIENCE DID AS WELL. WOMEN BEGAN TO USE GENETIC ENHANCEMENTS TO BECOME THE PHYSICAL EQUALS OF THE MEN. IN TURN, MEN USED RADIATION TO RETAIN THEIR EDGE, AND BECAME INFERTILE.
HUMAN PARTHENOGENESIS BECAME AVAILABLE, AND POPULAR. THE GENDERS GREW MORE POLARIZED AND BEGAN TO LIVE APART.
TERRITORIAL DISPUTES BROKE OUT. THE WORLD BECAME DIVIDED.
BOTH SIDES HAD THE TECHNOLOGY TO BOMB EACH OTHER TO INFINITY. YET THAT WAS NOT THE PARADIGM THAT OUR WORLD FOLLOWED. VICTORIES MUST BE BODILY. PHYSICAL.

THAT WAS THE WHOLE POINT OF THE GENDER WARS. TO DECIDE WHICH WAS THE TRUE POWER. THE BETTER SEX.
YAAAGH!
THINKERS FROM THE HULK'S TIME WOULD SAY THE WHOLE ARGUMENT WAS FLAWED. PERHAPS.
WHAT'S TRUE FOR ONE AGE IS NOT FOR ANOTHER.

WHO--
THOOM
--DARES?
THUNDRA DARES, SAVAGE!

A WOMAN...?
YOU ARE ANOTHER ARMY TRICK! NO WOMAN CAN HIT HULK LIKE THAT.
YOU'RE RIGHT, BEAST. I AM NO WOMAN.

I AM ALL WOMEN.

HULK SEES.
ARMY SENT YOU. ARMY THINKS HULK WILL NOT HIT A WOMAN.
GOOD PLAN.

BUT ARMY IS WRONG.
WE WILL BE EDITING THAT PART OUT.
HRRRAAH!
INCREDIBLE.

BANNER IS YOUR NAME.

THERE IS ***NO BANNER!***

BIO-SCAN COMPLETE.
SUBJECT IS A VIABLE CANDIDATE FOR PROCEDURE.

SUBJECT IS A VIABLE CANDIDATE FOR PROCEDURE.
SOMEONE IS TRYING TO TRICK HULK!

DO NOT DESTROY THE RECORDER!

HHRRRR!
RECKLESS FOOL!

AH!

FROM THE SECRET LOGS OF THE RECORDER, IT'S KNOWN THAT THUNDRA DOUBTED HERSELF. SHE HAD FINALLY TAKEN ON TOO POWERFUL AN OPPONENT.

THEN AGAIN, THAT WAS THE WHOLE POINT OF THE MISSION.

EEEYAHH!
THAT HER OBJECTIVES WERE ALSO THE ICONS OF MALE HISTORY PROVIDED A USEFUL COVER FOR THE PUBLIC.
THOR, THE THUNDER GOD, WOULD BE TOO DIFFICULT TO FIND WITH THE CHRONO-GATE.
GRIMM HAD PLEDGED LOYALTY TO ANOTHER, AND WAS MORE HONORABLE THAN OTHER MEN TO THAT END.
THE HULK HAD NO SUCH LOYALTIES, AND WAS EVER BOUND TO THE EARTH.
AND MANY STILL BELIEVE THAT ABOVE ALL, HE WAS STRONGEST. THE OBJECTIVE HAD TO BE HIM.

HUNDREDS OF THOUSANDS OF TONS OF ROCK.
IT SLOWED YOU DOWN, BUT DID NOT STOP YOU.
NOW YOU PRETEND TO HELP...ANOTHER TRICK!
NO, NO TRICKS. I KNOW I CANNOT BEAT YOU.
WHO ARE YOU? WHY ARE YOU SO STRONG?!
I AM THUNDRA, THE LEADER OF MY PEOPLE.
I AM FROM A PLACE WHERE WOMEN ARE MUCH STRONGER.
NO MAN THERE IS WORTHY OF ME. I HAVE COME A LONG WAY TO FIND SUCH A MAN.
HULK IS NOT A MAN! IF YOU WERE FROM HERE, YOU WOULD KNOW!
THE HULK IS A ***MONSTER.***

THAT MAKES IT MUCH BETTER.
WELL? DID IT TAKE?
YES. THE CELL SAMPLES YOU SCRAPED FROM INSIDE HIS CHEEK WERE COMPLIANT WITH OUR PROCESS.
AND...YES! THE GAMETES ARE FUSED.
YOU ARE THE FIRST WOMAN IN FOUR GENERATIONS TO BECOME PREGNANT.
THAT WAS TWENTY YEARS AGO.
SHE KNEW THAT SHE COULDN'T LEAD THE WOMEN OF EARTH FOREVER. AND TO APPOINT ANYONE LESS POWERFUL AS MATRIARCH WOULD BE THE DEATH OF THE SISTERHOOD.

THUNDRA DOES NOT COMMAND THE SHEER RAW FORCE SHE ONCE DID, BUT IT IS ENOUGH TO PROTECT THE WESTERN TERRITORIES.

ALLOWING ME TO EXPAND THE BORDERS. RECAPTURE LAND. AND MOVE FORWARD.
PUT HER DOWN!
SHE MUST NOT REACH THE TOWER!

OUR WEAKNESS WAS THAT WE ALWAYS FOUGHT A DEFENSIVE WAR, AND THAT KIND OF BATTLE CAN NEVER BE WON.

TO BEAT MEN, YOU HAVE TO PUSH AS THEY DO. ACTIVELY SEEK TO CONQUER.
AGGH!
NO!

AND NEVER SHOW MERCY.

MUCH TALK AMONG THE SISTERS SAYS THAT WE ACHIEVED THIS BY TAKING THAT TRAIT FROM THE MEN. AS IF MY MOTHER WERE PROMETHEUS, STEALING FIRE FROM THE GODS.
AFTER ALL, DIDN'T THIS POWER COME FROM THE ORIGINAL IRRADIATED MAN? THE WALKING NUCLEAR EXPLOSION? HOW CAN PEACE COME FROM THE SAME PLACE AS WAR, THEY ARGUE.
BUT I HAVE STUDIED ALL OF THE HISTORIES OF THE 21st CENTURY TITAN KNOWN AS HULK. DESPITE HIS LEGENDARY RAMPAGES, EVERYTHING I'VE FOUND ON THE MOST POWERFUL MAN--HUMAN--TO EVER EXIST... SAYS THAT HE WAS NO CONQUEROR.
JUST A PERSON WHO WANTED TO BE LEFT ALONE.
IN THAT RESPECT, I FEEL I KNOW HIM.

WHAT MY FATHER WANTED IS WHAT I WANT NOW. YET THE MEN OF MY TIME WILL NEVER STOP ATTACKING UNTIL THEY EXIST NO LONGER.
SO I WILL SEE THAT DAY COME TO PASS. AFTER THAT, WHO CAN SAY? CERTAINLY, THE FIRST PEACE THE WORLD HAS KNOWN IN MANY YEARS.
IN TIME, PERHAPS THE ATROCITIES OF MEN WILL FADE FROM THE WORLD'S MEMORY. PERHAPS FUTURE GENERATIONS WILL CREDIT MY FATHER WITH CONTRIBUTING TO THAT OUTCOME. AND MAYBE THOSE WOMEN WILL DECIDE THAT THE Y CHROMOSOME CAN RETURN TO THE WORLD.
IT SEEMS IMPOSSIBLE TO US NOW, LIKE SCIENCE FICTION.
WHO KNOWS WHAT THE FUTURE HOLDS?

FANTASTIC FOUR

MARVEL COMICS GROUP™

20¢ 133 APR 02462

THE WORLD'S GREATEST COMIX MAGAZINE!

FANTASTIC FOUR®

Stan Lee PRESENTS: THE FANTASTIC FOUR! TM
GERRY CONWAY, SCRIPTER / RAMONA FRADON, GUEST ARTIST / JOE SINNOTT, INKER / LETTERED BY: JOHN COSTANZA / COLORED BY: STAN GOLDBERG / PLOTTED AND EDITED BY: ROY THOMAS
THUNDRA at DAWN!
HAPPY NEW YEAR
42 ST.
TIMES SQ
GROWING FAMILIES
SWELL BUNCHA JOKERS WE ARE.
IT'S ALMOST MIDNIGHT ON NEW YEAR'S EVE-- WE'RE IN TIMES SQUARE-- AN' BETWEEN THE FIVE OF US, WE CAN'T CRACK ONE CRUMMY SMILE.
GREAT IDEA YA HAD, STRETCHO. ALMOST WISH I'D STAYED HOME AN' WATCHED GUY LOMBARDO ON THE TUBE.
YEAH,... ALMOST.
HAPPY NE
BEFORE THE EVENING'S OUT, YOU MIGHT REPEAT THAT WISH, BEN GRIMM.
THOUGH THINGS SEEM A BIT DOMESTIC RIGHT NOW, THERE'S DISASTER IN THE CARDS ...AND FRIEND, THAT'S AN UNDERSTATEMENT--!

WE'RE LIKE A GANG OF UNDERTAKERS...
...'CEPT YOU, ALICIA. AND YOU'RE THE ONLY ONE WITH REAL PROBLEMS...
BECAUSE I'M BLIND, BEN?
THAT'S NO PROBLEM...WHEN YOU'RE MY EYES.
AIN'T MUCH GOOD AT THAT, AM I?
I'M SUPPOSED TA BE TELLIN' YA WHAT'S HAPPENING-- AND HERE I GO PLAYIN' GLOOMY GUS.
SORRY, KID... THAT'S WHAT YA GET FOR HANGIN' AROUND THE THING.
TIMES SQ.
OND
HAPPY NEW YEAR
I'M WITH YOU BECAUSE I WANT TO BE.
I CARE ABOUT YOU... NOT YOUR MOODS.
HAVE A BALLOON, KID...
HAPPY NEW YEAR
ON ME, THEY LOOK KINDA FUNNY.
BEN, DON'T TALK LIKE THAT.

HARSH HUMOR: IT'S JUST ONE METHOD OF COPING WITH PAIN.
AND WHAT OF THE OTHER MEMBERS OF THIS SOMBER QUINTET? WHAT OF REED RICHARDS, FOR EXAMPLE--?
RICHARDS, WHOSE WIFE HAS LEFT HIM, TAKING THEIR CHILD--
--RICHARDS, WHO STANDS IN A SEA OF JOYFUL HUMANITY-- AND FIGHTS TO REMAIN AN ISLE.

DON'T TRY TO CHEER ME, MEDUSA.
FROM WHERE I STAND--THERE HASN'T BEEN MUCH GOOD IN 1972--
42 S
MES SQ
--AND THERE'S NOT LIKELY TO BE MUCH MORE IN '73.

SO THIS IS THE BRILLIANT REED RICHARDS? THE YOUNGEST INHUMAN SHOWS GREATER MATURITY THAN YOU HAVE--!
YOU, ONE OF MANKIND'S FINEST MINDS--
--OVERCOME WITH CHILDISH SELF-PITY!

SHE'S RIGHT, JOHNNY--WE'VE ALL BEEN TOO WITHDRAWN.
IN ANOTHER MINUTE WE'LL HIT THE NEW YEAR--NEW BEGINNINGS--PERHAPS A NEW LIFE.
SURE, REED--

I JUST WISH I COULD BE CERTAIN IT'LL BE A BETTER LIFE.
ME AND CRYSTAL--I THOUGHT WE WERE GOING TO BE A TEAM. IT'S TAKING SOME GETTING USED TO--
--KNOWING THAT SOME OTHER GUY'S WITH HER NOW--
--AND THAT, PRETTY SOON, JOHNNY STORM'S JUST GONNA BE A GUY SHE KNEW--
--ONCE--A LONG TIME AGO.

YA KNOW, KID--IT'S FUNNY. A FREAK LIKE ME--AN' I'M THE ONLY BUM HERE WITH THE GIRL HE LOVES.
GETS YA THINKIN', DON'T IT?

NO, BEN... IT ONLY MAKES ME REALIZE HOW FORTUNATE I AM...
...TO HAVE THE MOST WONDERFUL MAN OF ALL.
YEAH... WITH A MUG THAT BUSTS MIRRORS.
BEN, YOU'LL NEVER UNDERSTAND--AND THAT'S WHY I LOVE YOU.

HEY, COOK! IT'S ALMOST TWELVE O'CLOCK.
PRETTY SOON THAT GOLD BALL'S GONNA DROP--
--AN' IT'S 1973!

1973! THINK ABOUT IT, JOHNNY--THREE QUARTERS OF A CENTURY!
LORD, HOW THINGS HAVE CHANGED SINCE 1900...

PERHAPS THE WORLD ISN'T PERFECT YET, SON-- I DON'T KNOW IF WE'D LIKE IT IF IT WERE--
BUT IT'S BETTER NOW THAN BEFORE-- AND IF WE ALL KEEP TRYING--!
I STILL CAN'T BE SURE I AGREE WITH YOU, REED...
BUT, IF YOU CAN SMILE, WITH YOUR KINDA TROUBLES, SO CAN I... I GUESS...

YET-- EVEN AS JOHNNY STORM'S FLAGGING SPIRITS LIFT--
--THE SURROUNDING CROWD GROWS HUSHED--
--AND STARES-- IN STUNNED ASTONISHMENT!

THAT GIRL!
GOOD LORD-- SHE'S HOLDING BACK THE HANDS OF THE CLOCK--!
WHO IS SHE? HOW IN THE NAME OF HEAVEN DID SHE GET UP THERE?

HOLY COW!
IT'S THUNDRA!
THUNDRA! MYSTERIOUS NEW MEMBER OF THE GROUP CALLED THE FRIGHTFUL FOUR--
THUNDRA! WHOSE MISSION BECOMES APPARENT, AS--

BENJAMIN GRIMM! WHEREVER YOU ARE-- I CHALLENGE YOU!
I CHALLENGE YOU-- TO A DUEL YOU CAN NEVER WIN!
LOOK-- THE NEON SIGN AROUND THE ALLIED CHEMICAL BUILDING--
IT'S PRINTING OUT SOME SORT OF MESSAGE!

SHE WANTS TO BATTLE YOU, BEN-- IN SHEA STADIUM--AT DAWN-- THREE DAYS FROM NOW!
SHEESH! SHE HADDA GO TELL EVERYBODY?
SHE MUST NOT KNOW WE'RE IN THE CROWD, BEN--!

OBVIOUSLY, SHE HOPED TO ATTRACT OUR ATTENTION--
--AND SHE'S DONE THAT-- REMARKABLY WELL!

FIGURES YA'D SEE IT THAT WAY, BIG-WORDS.
THE WAY IT LOOKS TA ME-- SHE'S TRYIN' TA PUT ME ON THE SPOT.
AN' THOUGH OL' BLUE-EYED BENJY AIN'T NEVER HIT A WOMAN--

--BUT THIS TIME I MIGHT JUST MAKE ME AN EXCEPTION!

BEN GRIMM-- NO!
NOW IS NEITHER THE TIME-- NOR THE PLACE!
THAT'S RIGHT, BEN. YOU CAN'T--
FORGET IT, BOSS-MAN!
THIS IS MY FIGHT-- AN' I'LL FIGHT IT MY WAY!

YOU'D BETTER STAY BACK HERE, ALICIA.
I'VE GOT A FEELING THINGS ARE GOING TO GET KIND OF TENSE IN A MOMENT OR TWO!

AND IF THEY DO--
--JOHNNY STORM'S GOING TO BE WHERE THE ACTION IS--

--AND SO'S THE HUMAN TORCH!

JOHNNY, WAIT!
THIS ISN'T THE WAY!
TELL ME WHAT IS, LEADER-MAN!
I'VE BEEN CLIMBING THE WALLS FOR A WEEK, NOW--

--AND IT'S ABOUT TIME I LET LOOSE-- THE ONLY WAY I KNOW HOW!
YOU! THE FLAMING ONE--
IF YOU ARE HERE--THEN SO MUST BE-- THE THING!

DON'T LET IT WORRY YOU, LADY.
BEN'S A BIT TIED UP-- BUT IF YOU'VE GOT A PROBLEM -- I'M ALL EARS!
I'VE NO TIME TO WASTE WITH STRIPLINGS!

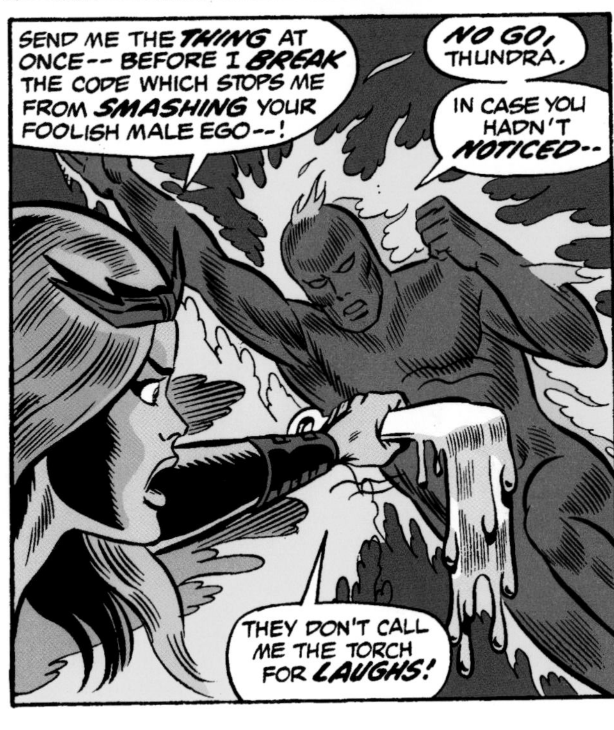
SEND ME THE THING AT ONCE-- BEFORE I BREAK THE CODE WHICH STOPS ME FROM SMASHING YOUR FOOLISH MALE EGO--!
NO GO, THUNDRA.
IN CASE YOU HADN'T NOTICED--
THEY DON'T CALL ME THE TORCH FOR LAUGHS!

REED ONCE TOLD ME I COULD RAISE MY BODY HEAT TO ONE THOUSAND DEGREES!
LET'S JUST TRY A FRACTION OF THAT--
--AND SEE IF IT MAKES YOU A LITTLE MORE FRIENDLY!
THE HEAT-- INCREDIBLE--

AN IMPRESSIVE DISPLAY--
--YET ULTIMATELY--A FUTILE ONE!
RRIPP
YOU MALES UNDERESTIMATE THE STRENGTH OF THUNDRA--

-- A STRENGTH WHICH MORE THAN EQUALS THE THING'S OWN!
SWOOOSH!
YOU'RE MISSING ME BY A MILE, SISTER--

--OR ARE YOU?
NOW I UNDERSTAND! YOU DIDN'T WANT TO HIT ME--!

SWISH!
YOU'RE SPINNING THAT CLOCK ARROW LIKE A BLADE PROPELLOR--
--BLOWING OUT MY FLAME!
AND WITHOUT MY FLAME-- I CAN'T FLY!
I'LL FALL!

EVERYTHING'S MOVING TOO QUICKLY--
BEN, YOU'VE GOT TO STOP HER!
NOW HE TELLS ME!
WHAT'S WRONG WITH YOU, BIG BRAINS?
YOU GOTTA HAVE A HOUSE FALL ON YA OR SUMTHIN'?

YOU ARRIVE TOO LATE, BENJAMIN GRIMM.
MUCH AS IT PAINS ME TO HARM A MEMBER OF THE WEAKER SEX--
--THE TORCH MUST BE ELIMINATED-- AT ONCE!
JOHNNY! NO!

YEARS OF TRAINING-- INSTINCTIVE REFLEX:
IN ONE STARTLING SPLIT SECOND, THE TWO JOIN TOGETHER--

REED RICHARD'S ELASTIC ARMS REACH OUT-- MEDUSA'S NEAR-SENTIENT SCARLET COILS WRITHE AND TWINE--
--AND THE FALLING JOHNNY STORM IS SAVED--
TIMES SQ.
--BY A HAIR!*
*SORRY, GANG. --SHEEPISH GER.

BUT MEANWHILE...
MY APOLOGIES, BENJAMIN GRIMM. I'D ALMOST PREFER TO CRUSH YOU NOW--
--BUT MY PLANS DEMAND I POSTPONE THAT DUTY--FOR THREE DAYS!
YEAH? AN' WHAT IF I DON'T GO ALONG?
WHAT IF I SAY NO?

I HARDLY THINK YOU'LL REFUSE, MAN-MONSTER!
NOT WITH THE LIFE OF YOUR FEMALE AT STAKE!
BEN--WHAT'S HAPPENING--?

QUIET, WOMAN!
DO YOU WANT THOSE MEN TO THINK YOU'RE WEAK?
BEN!
SHE GOT ALICIA-- CARRYIN' HER OFF ON THAT FLYIN' DISK!
ALICIA-- BABY--!

DO NOT DISAPPOINT ME, BENJAMIN GRIMM!
THREE DAYS FROM TODAY-- AT DAWN! BATTLE ME-- OR THE WOMAN DIES!
A STUNNED HUSH SETTLES OVER THE ONLOOKING CROWD-- A SILENCE SUDDENLY BROKEN BY--

ALICIA, HONEY!
I WON'T LET YA DOWN!
I'LL SAVE YA, KID-- I PROMISE YA THAT--

WE'LL BACK YOU UP-- ALL THE WAY, OLD FRIEND.
DON'T WORRY, BEN--
BUT RIGHT NOW-- WE'D BETTER GET BACK TO THE BAXTER BUILDING-- AND SEE IF WE CAN TRACE THUNDRA!

TWAING!
AND THAT MEANS TRAVELING--
AS FAST AS WE CAN!

AMSTER
FIZZ CO
HEY, D.W.-- TAKE A GLANCE OUT THE WINDOW!
AIN'T THAT A SIGHT?

THE FANTASTIC FOUR-- FLYIN' RIGHT ON BY LUKE CAGE--*
--AN' NOT EVEN STOPPIN' FOR A DUDE'S AUTOGRAPH!
*WHO HERE DOESN'T KNOW MARVEL'S OWN HERO FOR HIRE? --R.T.

IT'S AN EVEN TEN BLOCKS FROM TIMES SQUARE TO THE MIDTOWN OFFICE BUILDING THE FF USES AS A HEADQUARTERS--
--TEN BLOCKS COVERED IN LESS THAN TEN SECONDS!
Drink MILK
STEAK
LICATESSEN
EAT
YET, NOT ONE OF THE FOUR FEELS JOY-- FOR THEY KNOW THAT SUCH TIME-SAVING IS MERELY AN ILLUSION--
--ONE THAT ONLY CONCEALS THE DEADLY DANGER YET TO COME!

...LATE LAST NIGHT, AND SINCE THAT TIME SPECULATION ABOUT THURSDAY'S DAWN BATTLE HAS GROWN INCREASINGLY DRAMATIC.
ALREADY, THE CITY'S OFF-TRACK BETTING CORPORATION HAS ISSUED ODDS ON THE FIGHT--
-- AND MANY OF THE NATION'S LEADING NEWSPAPERS HAVE JOINED IN A JOURNALISTIC RACE TO GARNER THE WIDEST OPINION ON THE SUBJECT!
VS
THUN
7-5
DAILY LEDGE
BATTLE SET FOR
15¢
MORNING LEDGE
FIGHT OF THE CENTURY

"EVEN SO, MANY OF THE MORE PUBLIC SUPER-HEROES -- SUCH AS THE WORLD-FAMOUS AVENGERS -- HAVE REFUSED TO COMMENT ON THE UPCOMING CONFLICT--
"--THOUGH THEY MUST CERTAINLY BE AWARE OF IT!"
WELL? WHAT DO YOU THINK, THOR?
'TIS MADNESS-- NO MORE.
DAILY SUN
THUNDRA VS THING
VERILY, THE WAYS OF MORTALS DO CONTINUE TO ASTOUND ME!

...THE THING VERSUS THAT THUNDRA CHICK, HM?
MUCH AS I LIKE OLD BENJY*, I HATE TO ADMIT IT -- BUT MY MONEY'S ON THE LADY!
* BEN AND SPIDEY MET IN TEAM-UP #7. --RT.

HULK DOESN'T UNDERSTAND. PICTURES SAY FIGHT.
WHY GIRL WANT TO HIT ROCK-THING? MAKE HULK'S HEAD HURT.
FIGHT DUMB.
EVERYONE DUMB.

AYE, OPINION RUNS STRONG ACROSS THE COUNTRY--
--BUT CERTAINLY NO STRONGER THAN IT DOES IN AN ABANDONED WATER TOWER IN QUEENS--

--WHERE--
LOSIN' YER NERVE, GIRLIE?
HARDLY. I'M MERELY AMUSED BY THIS WOMAN'S FAITH IN HER MALE.
SHE BELIEVES HE'LL BEAT ME.
1000
500
SHE DOES, HUH?

SHE BETTER NOT GO GETTIN HER HOPES UP. WE PROMISED TA SET YA UP WITH THE WORLD'S STRONGEST MAN--
--AN' AFTER YA HANDLE HIM-- WHY-- THERE AIN'T MUCH NEED FOR HER TA HANG AROUND, IS THERE?

SIMPERING MALE!
HOW DARE YOU EVEN INSINUATE I'D ALLOW SUCH A THING?
WHOK!

HOLD, THUNDRA-- THE WINGLESS WIZARD COMMANDS IT!
AS FOR YOU, SANDMAN--
IN THE FUTURE-- TRY TO MAINTAIN A CERTAIN DIGNITY.
YOUR CRUDENESS IS UNBEFITTING OF THE FRIGHTFUL FOUR!

THE FRIGHTFUL FOUR--A COLLECTION OF NEAR-POWERLESS MEN.
WITHOUT THUNDRA, YOUR STRENGTH WOULD BE LESS THAN A QUARTER OF WHAT IT IS!
THAT MAY BE--
500
--BUT I ASSURE YOU--YOU'LL FIND THE THING SOME-WHAT MORE PHYSICAL THAN WE--UNLESS YOU PRE-PARE YOURSELF, AS PLANNED!

HAVE PATIENCE, MY FRIENDS. AT THE MOMENT-- WE REQUIRE HER AID.
SOON, HOWEVER--CONDITIONS WILL CHANGE.
YES, INDEED.

HEY, BENJY-- TAKE IT EASY.
YOU'VE ALREADY CRUNCHED SIX OF THOSE BABIES.
YA AIN'T SEEN NUTHIN'! TORCHIE.

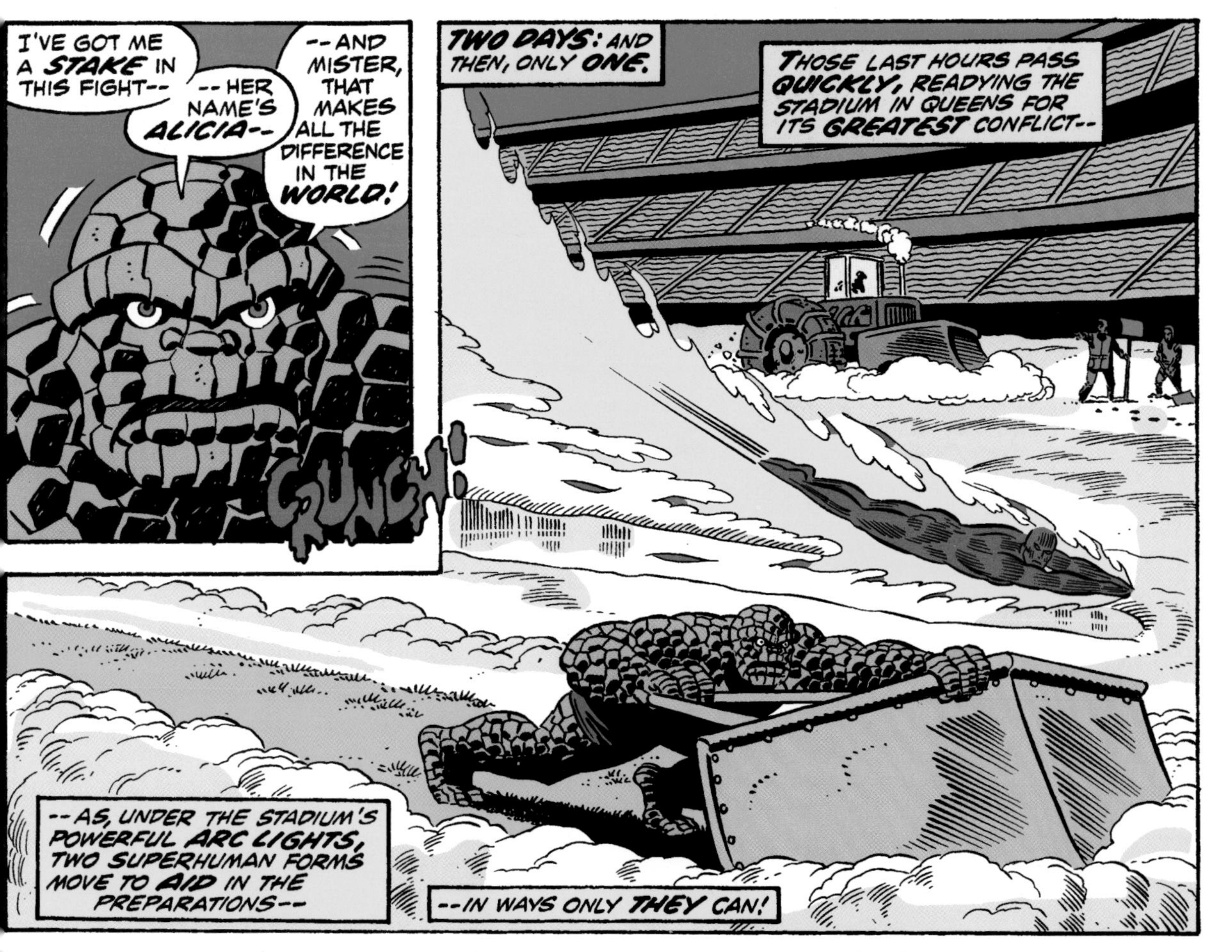
I'VE GOT ME A STAKE IN THIS FIGHT--
--HER NAME'S ALICIA--
--AND MISTER, THAT MAKES ALL THE DIFFERENCE IN THE WORLD!
CRUNCH!
TWO DAYS: AND THEN, ONLY ONE.
THOSE LAST HOURS PASS QUICKLY, READYING THE STADIUM IN QUEENS FOR ITS GREATEST CONFLICT--
--AS, UNDER THE STADIUM'S POWERFUL ARC LIGHTS, TWO SUPERHUMAN FORMS MOVE TO AID IN THE PREPARATIONS--
--IN WAYS ONLY THEY CAN!

THEN, THE MOMENT ARRIVES. DAWN IS BUT AN HOUR AWAY-- THE MORNING AIR IS CRISP WITH WINTER--
--AND LOUD WITH THE VOICES OF THE THRONGS GATHERED TO VIEW THE COMING BATTLE.
TO VIEW-- AND TO WAGER, AS WELL!
WE LOVE THUNDRA

WELL, GRIMM... THIS IS IT.
YA CAN'T PUT IT OFF ANY LONGER.

...'CAUSE THIS IS THE ONE THAT COUNTS.

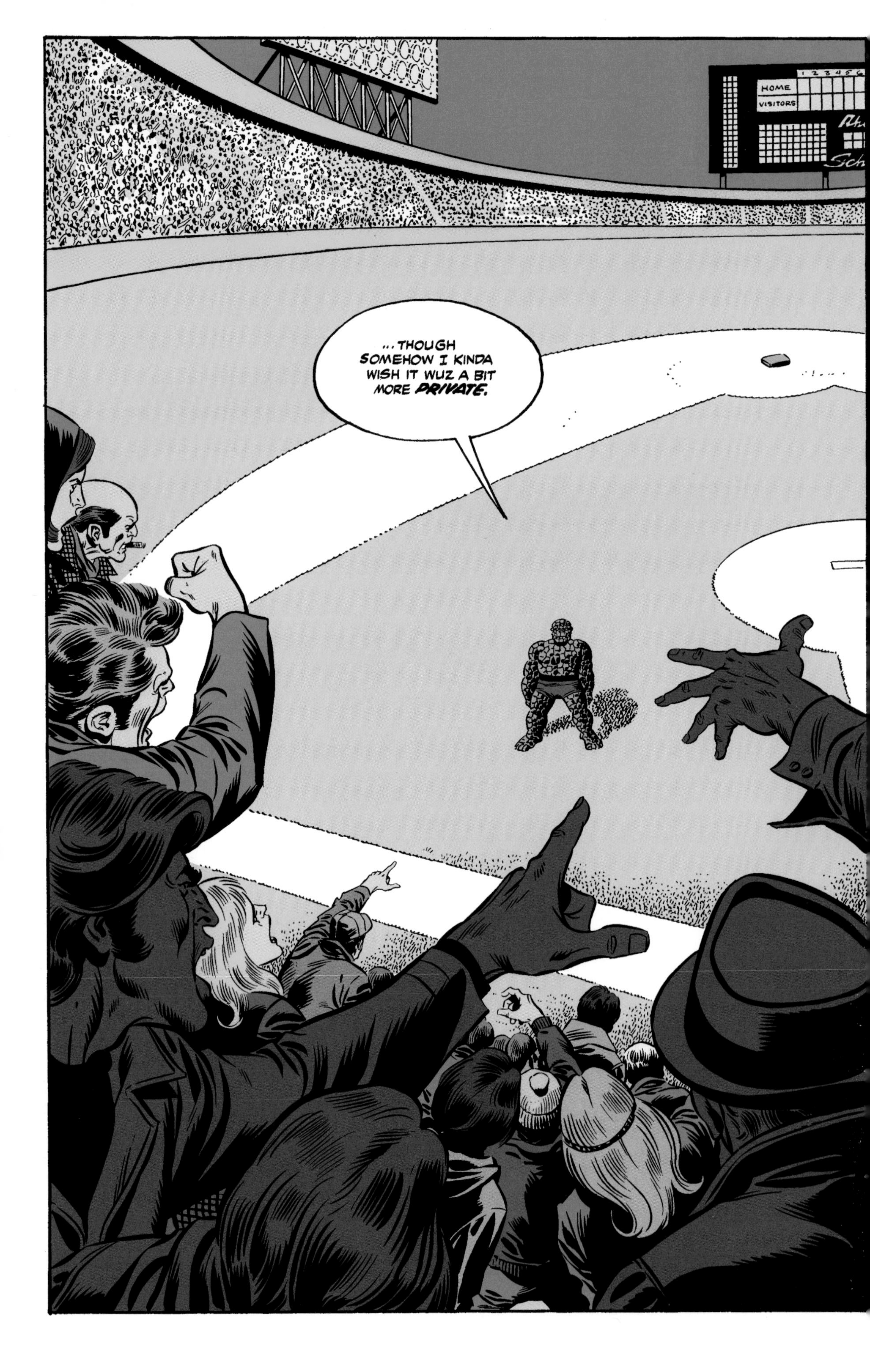
...THOUGH SOMEHOW I KINDA WISH IT WUZ A BIT MORE PRIVATE.
HOME
VISITORS

PRIVACY WOULD NOT SUIT MY PURPOSE, BENJAMIN GRIMM.
THE DEFEAT OF EARTH'S STRONGEST MALE IS SOMETHING I WISH THE WORLD TO WITNESS--
--FOR REASONS--ALL MY OWN!
I'LL BET YER GREAT AT RALLIES, MUSCLE-LADY.

THUNDRA...THING...I'VE BEEN APPOINTED BY THE MAYOR TO REFEREE THIS...AH... BATTLE.
NOW, I WANT YOU TWO TO SHAKE HANDS, AND--

LITTLE MAN--I CAME HERE TO BEAT THE THING--
--NOT TO PLAY GAMES--WITH YOU!

SHEESH! IF YA DIDN'T WANNA GO ACCORDIN' TO THE RULES--WHY DIDN'T YA JUST SAY SO?
I'LL TRY'N MAKE THIS PRETTY EASY ON YA--I AIN'T NEVER FOUGHT A GAL BEFORE, REALLY--
YOU BUMBLING MALE--

YOU STILL DON'T REALIZE--THUNDRA IS STRONGER THAN YOU--
--SHE IS STRONGER THAN ANY MAN ALIVE!
OOOCH!

AND I INTEND TO EXPOSE YOUR PITIABLE MALE INFERIORITY--

--NOW!

UH-HUH.
SOME DAYS IT JUST DON'T PAY TA GET OUTTA BED.

FOR AN INSTANT THE CROWD SITS STUNNED--
THUNDRA

--AND IN THAT INSTANT, THUNDRA STEPS ABOARD THE DISK GIVEN HER BY THE WIZARD--
--AND SAILS TO MEET HER PREY!
TEN BUCKS A SEAT!
ADMIT 1
WHAT A ROOK!

LOOKS LIKE THUNDRA'S GOT HER AUDIENCE ANGRY, REED!
LET'S JUST HOPE THAT'S ALL SHE'S DONE, JOHNNY!
MEDUSA--WE'VE GOT TO FIND THEM! BEN MAY NEED OUR HELP!

SOME PLAN YOU HAD, WIZ. SO WE WERE GONNA BLOW UP THE STADIUM AND GET BOTH OF 'EM, HUH?
BEN? IS HE ALL RIGHT?
SNUT UP, YOU FOOL. TAKE THE GIRL BACK TO HEADQUARTERS.
SANDMAN AND I WILL LOOK FOR OUR WAYWARD FRIEND.
FOR NOW, SISTER... FOR NOW.

GOTTA DO THIS JUST RIGHT--
--OTHERWISE THERE'S GONNA BE SPLATTERED BENJAMIN GRIMM ALL OVER THE FLUSHING SUBWAY!
:EEEEYOW!:
IF I WUZ A KID-- I'D THINK THIS WUZ GREAT--
--BUT RIGHT NOW THOUGH-- IT'S GIVIN' ME ONE HECK OF A BLASTED HEADACHE!
WHUPS. EXCUSE ME, PAL-- BUT I'D FORGOTTEN ABOUT YA.
JUST LIKE THIS TOWN TA KEEP A BUFFALO HERD IN FLUSHIN' MEADOW PARK!
GUESS IT'S SOMEBODY'S LAMEBRAIN IDEA OF CONSERVATION.
HUH? THUNDRA --ON TOP OF THE WORLD-GLOBE!*
*A RENOWNED RELIC OF THE 1964-65 NEW YORK WORLD'S FAIR! --RT
WELL--YOU JUST STAY THERE, SISTER.
OLD BENJY WON'T KEEP YA WAITIN' LONG!

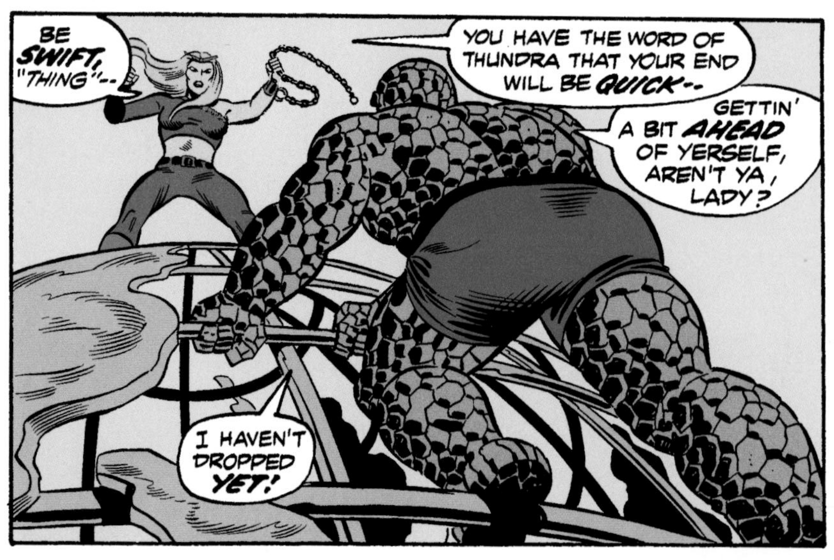
BE SWIFT, "THING"--
YOU HAVE THE WORD OF THUNDRA THAT YOUR END WILL BE QUICK--
GETTIN' A BIT AHEAD OF YERSELF, AREN'T YA, LADY?
I HAVEN'T DROPPED YET!

YOU WILL, BENJAMIN GRIMM.
THOUGH I PROMISE YOU-- I SHALL NOT TAKE UNDO ADVANTAGE OF YOUR SEX--!

THAT CUTS IT, SISTER!
I'VE HAD JUST ABOUT ENOUGH OF THIS "WEAKER SEX" BUNK!
ON THE CONTRARY, GRIMM--

YOU HAVEN'T EVEN BEEN TOUCHED!
ZOK!

NOW DO YOU CONCEDE?
DO YOU ADMIT THAT I'M MORE POWERFUL THAN YOU?

SISTER, I DON'T ADMIT NUTHIN'!
FAR AS I'M CONCERNED--WE AIN'T EVEN BEGUN TA FIGHT!

THAT IS WHERE YOU ARE MOST WRONG, BENJAMIN GRIMM.
FOR YOU-- THE BATTLE IS MOST DEFINITELY OVER!
SNAK!

EVERY NERVE SEEMS TO SNAP INSIDE THE SKULL OF THE MAN CALLED BENJAMIN GRIMM.
HE FINDS HIMSELF FALLING--

--AND ONLY HIS REFLEXES SAVE HIM--

--THOUGH IT SEEMS THAT SAVING IS ONLY A DELAY--
--FOR THE PAINFULLY INEVITABLE! AND THEN--

DO YOU CONCEDE?
NOT... ON... YER... LIFE.

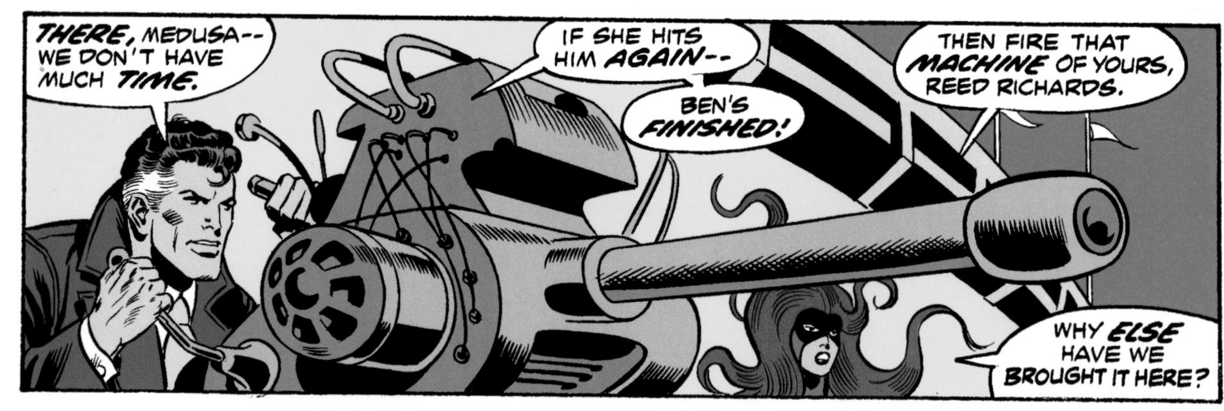
THERE, MEDUSA-- WE DON'T HAVE MUCH TIME.
IF SHE HITS HIM AGAIN--
BEN'S FINISHED!
THEN FIRE THAT MACHINE OF YOURS, REED RICHARDS.
WHY ELSE HAVE WE BROUGHT IT HERE?

ONE INSTANT: DIVIDED INTO ITS COMPONENT PARTS--
ZZEEEEE
--SPLIT BY A PIERCING, TRANSFORMING RAY DESIGNED BY THE BRILLIANT BRAIN OF A MAN CALLED RICHARDS--
--A RAY WHICH HAS A SOMEWHAT UNEXPECTED EFFECT ON THE FORM OF THE CREATURE WE KNOW AS-- THE THING!
NO! HE'S--HE'S BECOME HUMAN AGAIN!
I'VE BEEN CHEATED-- CHEATED!

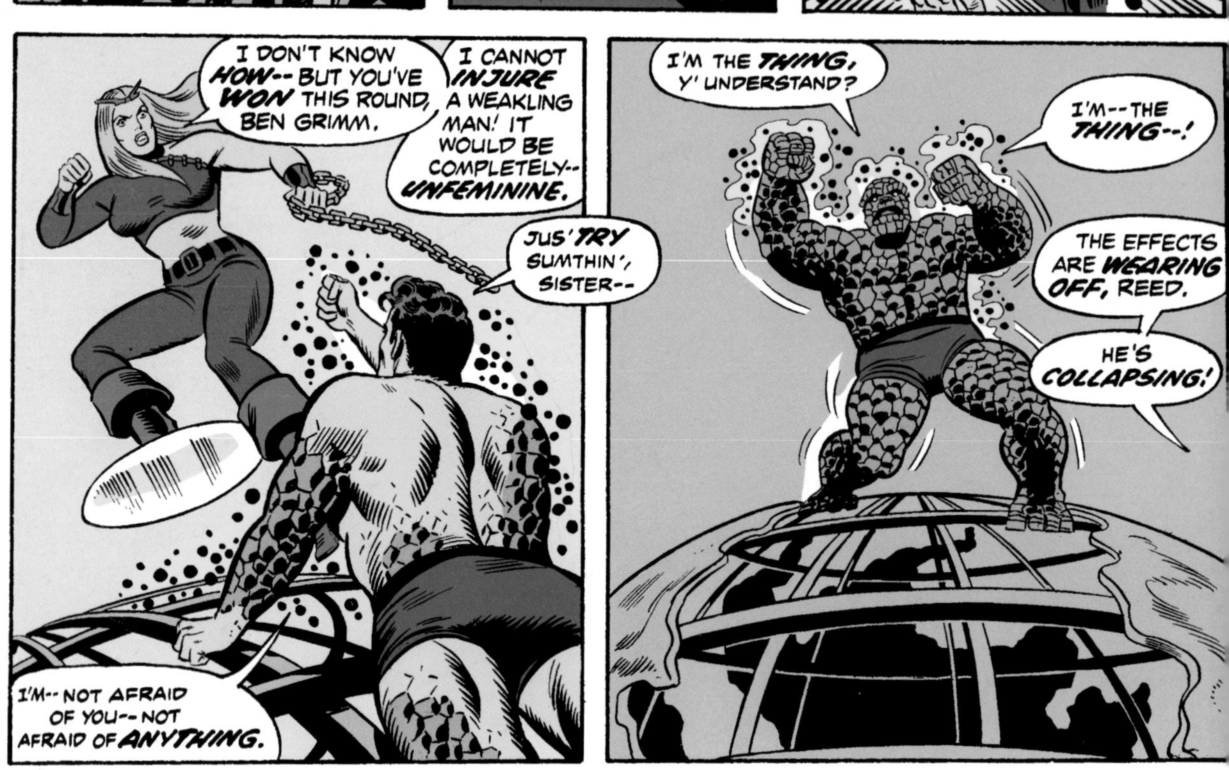
I DON'T KNOW HOW-- BUT YOU'VE WON THIS ROUND, BEN GRIMM.
I CANNOT INJURE A WEAKLING MAN! IT WOULD BE COMPLETELY-- UNFEMININE.
JUS' TRY SUMTHIN', SISTER--
I'M-- NOT AFRAID OF YOU-- NOT AFRAID OF ANYTHING.
I'M THE THING, Y' UNDERSTAND?
I'M--THE THING--!
THE EFFECTS ARE WEARING OFF, REED.
HE'S COLLAPSING!

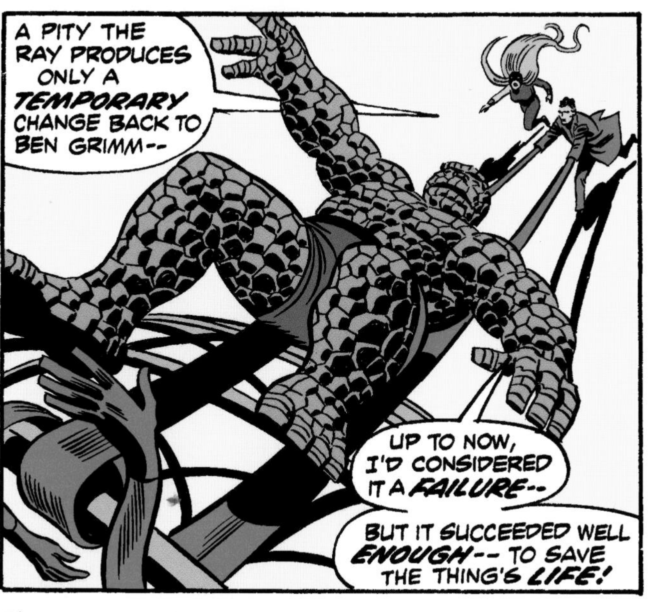

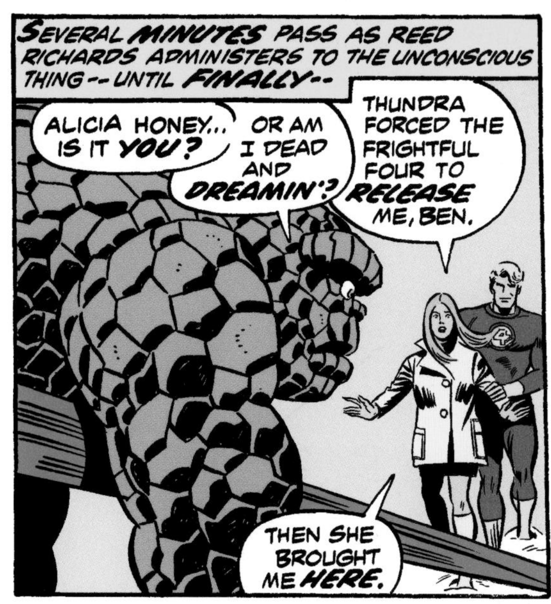

AND NOW, AN UNABASHED EPILOGUE:

HULK VS. HERCULES: WHEN TITANS COLLIDE #1

MORTALS WOULDST DO WELL TO PERUSE THE TOME OF

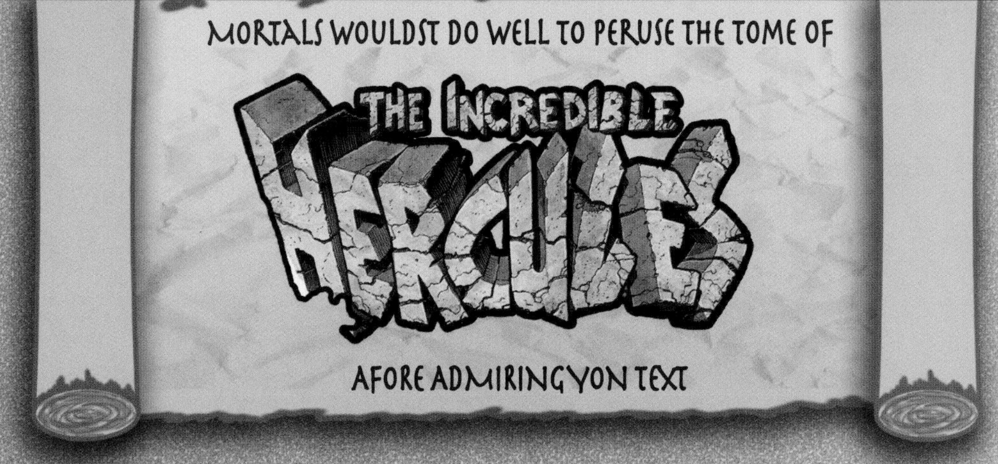

AFORE ADMIRING YON TEXT

WHILE TRYING TO SAVE THE LIFE OF AN INNOCENT, DOCTOR BRUCE BANNER WAS CAUGHT IN THE BLAST OF A GAMMA BOMB AND BECAME A RAMPAGING MONSTER WITH NEAR-LIMITLESS POWER:

FATHERED BY ZEUS, HERCULES IS A GOD AMONGST MEN, RIGHTING WRONGS AND DISPELLING EVILS. AND HE DRINKS BEER. CURRENTLY, HE IS ON THE RUN FROM THE MORTAL ENFORCEMENT AGENCY, S.H.I.E.L.D., ALONG WITH HIS SISTER, ATHENA, AND BOY GENIUS, AMADEUS CHO (WITH PUP IN TOW).

"SMASH OF THE TITANS"

GREG PAK & FRED VAN LENTE – WRITERS
KHOI PHAM, PAUL NEARY, DENNIS CALERO – ART PAGES 1-2, 31
ERIC NGUYEN – ART PAGES 3-7
REILLY BROWN, CARLOS CUEVAS, TERRY PALLOT, CHRIS SOTOMAYOR – ART PAGES 8, 11-30
BOB LAYTON, GURU EFX – ART PAGES 9-10
VC'S JOE CARAMAGNA – LETTERER
MARKO DJURDJEVIC – COVER
PAUL ACERIOS & ANTHONY DIAL – PRODUCTION
NATHAN COSBY – ASSISTANT EDITOR
MARK PANICCIA – EDITOR
JOE QUESADA – EDITOR IN CHIEF
DAN BUCKLEY – PUBLISHER

HULK SMASH PUNY SKIRT MAN!
PERUUUUUUUM
NAY! BY THE BEARD OF MIGHTY ZEUS, I SAY THEE--
--NUTS.
HAW.
GAME OVER!
SMASH of the TITANS
DA AA
DA DA
DA DA
DA AA

I HATE TO ADMIT IT, AMADEUS. BUT YOU'VE BESTED THE LION OF OLYMPUS.
THAT'S WHAT YOU GET FOR CHALLENGING SOMEONE THREE THOUSAND YEARS YOUNGER THAN YOU TO A VIDEO GAME.
AH, WELL. TODAY MY AGE WILL GET ME ONE THING YOURS CANNOT...

BEER!
HEH.
I DON'T GET IT.
BEER, ATHENA. YOU HAVE TO BE TWENTY-ONE TO BUY--
THAT I GET. IT'S THE REST OF IT THAT CONFUSES ME.

YOU PLAY THAT HULK GAME WITH MY BROTHER. AND NEITHER OF YOU SAY A WORD ABOUT WHAT YOU'VE JUST BEEN THROUGH.
WHAT'S TO SAY?
YOU WERE THE HULK'S GREATEST HAMPION, AMADEUS. YOU NEARLY DESTROYED S.H.I.E.L.D. FOR HOW THEY TREATED HIM...*
...AND NOW THAT WE'RE WITHIN TWO HUNDRED MILES OF THE DESERT ARMY BASE WHERE THE EWS REPORTS SAY HE'S BEING HELD, YOU'RE NOT DEMANDING WE RUN OFF TO HELP HIM AGAIN?
*SEE "INCREDIBLE HULK" #112 AND "INCREDIBLE HERCULES" #113-115, TRUE BELIEVERS!

MAYBE I LEARNED MY LESSON.
WHICH WAS...?
YOU'RE THE GODDESS OF WISDOM. YOU TELL ME.
YOU'RE THE SMARTEST KID ON THE PLANET. YOU TELL ME.

I...I CAN RUN THE NUMBERS. SO I COULD SEE HE WAS ALWAYS PULLING HIS PUNCHES, LOOKING OUT FOR THE LITTLE PEOPLE. BUT IN THE END...
...HE REALLY COULD HAVE KILLED US ALL.
HE WAS THE WRONG PERSON TO CHAMPION.

AND HERCULES IS THE RIGHT PERSON?
WELL. HE'S KINDA LIKE THE HULK. BUT WITH BETTER JOKES.
IF YOU THINK THAT'S TRUE...

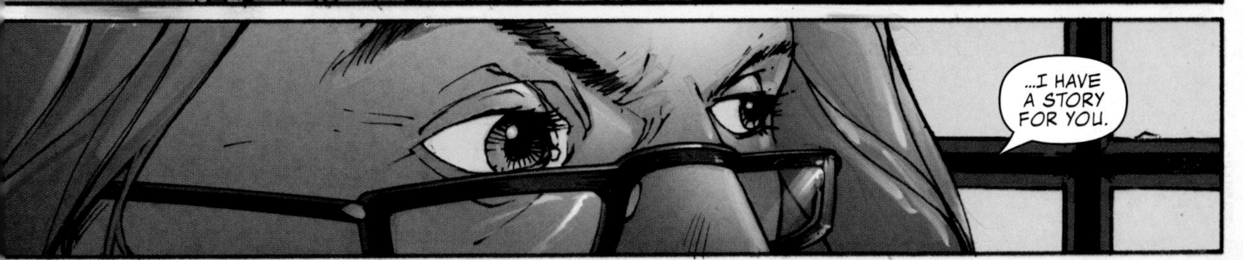
...I HAVE A STORY FOR YOU.

"BEHOLD GAEA! MOTHER EARTH HERSELF, BEAUTIFUL, KIND, AND CRUEL--"
"YEAH, YEAH, ALSO KNOWN AS NERTHA, ADITI, COATLIQUE, AND JORD. I THOUGHT THIS WAS A HERC STORY?"
"SHE GIVES BIRTH TO THOR, ONE OF THIS SAD MUDBALL'S GREATEST DEFENDERS--"
"LIKE I SAID, I THOUGHT THIS WAS--"
"--AND SHE MOTHERS DEMOGORGE THE GOD-EATER, WHO NEARLY DESTROYS THE PLANET THREE TIMES OVER."
"OKAY. LITTLE CONTRADICTIO THERE..."
"THEN, WHEN THE TITANS ENSLAVE THE CYCLOPES AGAIN, SHE HELPS THE GODS, HER BELOVED GRANDCHILDREN, AGAINST THE TITANS...

F I WERE A POET, I IGHT SAY THAT LIFE N ONLY FLOURISH IN IE WAKE OF DEATH.
"BUT I'VE LIVED TOO LONG FOR SUCH ASY COMFORT. SO I TELL YOU SIMPLY THAT THREE TIMES GAEA SENDS HER CHILDREN TO DESTROY HER CHILDREN.
"WHEN URANUS BANISHES THE CYCLOPES SHE BORE HIM, SHE SENDS HER TITANS AGAINST URANUS.
"...AND THEN, PITYING THE TITANS WHOM THE GODS SEALED UP IN THE DARK PRISON OF TARTARUS...
"...SHE SENDS THE GIANTS, HER NEWEST AND FIERCEST CHILDREN, TO SLAY THE GODS.
"BUT THE GODS TRIUMPH--THANKS TO MIGHTY HERCULES...
"...AND GLORY IN PROUD OLYMPUS WHILE GAEA'S POOR CHILDREN SUFFER IN DARKNESS...

"...UNTIL A NEW MONSTER RISES FROM THEIR AGONY.
"OVID SINGS THAT WHEN THE BLOOD OF GAEA'S GIANTS SPILLED ON THE EARTH, THE SAVAGE RACE OF MAN WAS BORN.

"NOW, MILLENNIA LATER, GAEA LETS HERSELF BELIEVE.
"FOR WHO COULD CHALLENGE THE ODINSON HIMSELF...
"...BUT THE NEWEST, MOST PERFECT, AND NOW...
"...MOST BELOVED OF HER OWN FIERCE CHILDREN?
PARK

"BUT BEFORE SHE CAN RAISE HER OWN HAND TO HELP THIS SAVAGE CHILD...
"...DOCTOR STRANGE THE SORCERER SUPREME OF THE MORTAL PLANE INTERVENES...
"...BANISHING THE HULK TO THE CROSSROADS, A MYSTIC LAND BETWEEN LANDS WHOSE MILLION PORTALS COULD LEAD THE HULK TO A MILLION DIFFERENT WORLDS.
"STRANGE'S SPELL IS MEANT TO HELP THE HULK--SENDING HIM TO SEARCH FOR A HOME- AND BRING HIM BACK T THE CROSSROADS TO T AGAIN SHOULD HE FIND HIMSELF UNHAPPY.
"BUT IN EACH NEW WORLD, THIS CHILD OF RAGE FINDS ONLY PAIN AND HATE AND FEAR.
"UNTIL GAEA FINALLY TAKES PITY...

RRR?
"...AND WE IN PROUD OLYMPUS...
RRRRR—
GRRAAAAAAAH!
BLABLAG
WAAAAAM
"...KNOW FEAR."
"OKAY. ONE LAST TIME...

MADISON SQUARE
U.C.W.F. PRESENTS:
HERCULES VS.
EVERYONE
"...WHERE'S HERC IN THIS STORY?"
U.C.W.F.
HA HA HA HA HA!!
YOU "UNLIMITED CLASS WRESTLING" AMATEURS ARE MOST AMUSING!
YOU ACTUALLY THOUGHT YOU COULD BEST THE MAN WHO, ALONG WITH SLY THESEUS, INVENTED THE NOBLE ART OF PANKRATION?
UCWF

COME NOW! IS THERE NO MORTAL WITHIN THIS CONCRETE COLOSSEUM WHO CAN LAST ONE ROUND WITH HERCULES?
'TIS FOR CANCER RESEARCH!
YOU WOULDN'T LAST FIVE MINUTES IN A YANCY STREET BLOCK FIGHT, CURLY!

BENJAMIN GRIMM! AT LAST--A WORTHY OPPONENT--
--AND A FITTING ONE, SINCE YOU ORGANIZED THESE BREAD AND CIRCUSES, DID YOU NOT?
VERY WELL, THEN: HAVE AT THEE!
YEAH, OR AS WE SAY IN AMERICAN:
IT'S CLOBBERIN' TIME!
IF BY "CLOBBERIN'" YOU MEAN LETTING YOU GET IN CLOSE ENOUGH FOR ME TO USE THE GASTRIZEIN...
OOF!
ZWOK!
...THEN AYE, I MOST HEARTILY AGREE!
THIS HEEL LOCK WAS NAMED AFTER FEARSOME ACHILLES, CONQUEROR OF TROY!
WHO WORSHIPPED MY BROTHER ARES, BUT I TRY NOT TO HOLD THAT AGAINST HIM...
AAAHH!
SEE, FRIEND GRIMM? YOUR STONY HIDE AVAILS YOU NAUGHT WHEN I USE YOUR OWN MIGHTY TENDONS AGAINST YOU!
GO...OPEN... A DINER, WHY DON'T'CHA...
HERO OF ALL HEROES! ENOUGH WITH MORTAL SPORT!
ZEUS PANHELLENIOS REQUIRES YOUR PRESENCE IN OLYMPUS--IMMEDIATELY!
VERY WELL, HERMES.
IF YOU SUMMON ME TO MORE CHALLENGING PASTIMES...

"...I SHALL GO WITH YOU GRATEFULLY AND GLADLY!"
ON GUARD, CALLIAS! I HEAR A STRANGER PUSH HIS WAY THROUGH THE BRAMBLES--
--BE HE A BUTCHER FROM OPPRESSIVE OLYMPUS?
NAY, BROTHER ZENO--HE LOOKS TO BE A FELLOW CHILD OF GAEA, GREEN AS THE EARTH MOTHER HERSELF.
COLOR MEANS LITTLE TO ME SINCE CURSED ZEUS BURNT AWAY MY SIGHT--BUT I TOO SENSE A KINDRED, NOBLE SPIRIT APPROACH.
SIT, COUSIN, DRINK, AND REGALE US WITH THE TALE OF ADVENTURE OR WOE THAT CONCLUDES WITH YOUR ARRIVAL TO OUR BLIGHTED SITE...
RRHHRR?
GULP GULP GULP
CALLIAS... METHINKS FROM HIS GUTTURAL TONE...OUR COUSIN IS WITHOUT THE BLESSINGS OF SPEECH.
HALF-MEN ARE WE ALL THEN, SINCE A THUNDERBOLT FROM THE GODS' TYRANT EXPLODED YOUR EYES...
...AND THE SAVAGE GOD OF WAR TORE MY SWORD ARM WHOLE FROM ITS SOCKET ON THAT SAME BATTLEFIELD.
'TIS THE ONLY REASON THE LEGIONS OF ZEUS SPARED OUR MANGLED LIVES WHILE THEY SLAUGHTERED OUR BRETHREN...

...AND CAST THEIR BROKEN BODIES INTO OOMY TARTARUS, BEHIND YON PRISON GATES.
TO HONOR OUR COMRADES AND KIN, WE TARRY HERE AT MEALTIME, AS WITH THIS DAY'S CAPTURED BOAR.
WE PRAY THE SUCCULENT SCENTS CARRY DOWN TO THE DEPTHS OF PLUTO'S DARK COUNTRY...
...AND REMIND OUR BROTHERS OF...HAPPIER TIMES.
SO THAT'S WHAT BECAME OF OUR PRIZE.
WE'VE BEEN RACKING THAT CALYDONIAN BOAR FOR DAYS.
AND I'LL E DAMNED IF 'LL LET A PAIR OF GIMPY ANTS STEAL IT FROM US.
IS THAT WISE, ARES?
IT WOULD APPEAR THE MONSTROUS HULK OF THE MORTAL AVENGERS* ENJOYS THEIR HOSPITALITY.
AND IF IT WAS HIS RAGE THAT SHOOK THE PILLARS OF OLYMPUS BUT A MOMENT AGO, DON'T YOU THINK--
I THINK YOU ARE A WOMAN, ATHENA.
AND YOU THINK WOMANLY THOUGHTS.
HMP.
TOUCHÉ.
*GREENSKIN & THE ASSEMBLERS TRAVELED TO OLYMPUS IN AVENGERS #100. BUT YOU KNEW THAT.-- M. "I ♥ CONTINUITY" PANICCIA & N. "OLD COMICS" COSBY

ZENO! CALLIAS!
THAT VOICE-- BRIMMING WITH BLOODLUST-- BROTHER, TELL ME IT'S NOT--
WHAT USE HAVE I FOR SUCH OFFAL?
NAY, VANQUISHED ONES, YOU HAVE CLAIMED GAME MARKED FOR ME.
PWAMM!
AYE, THE BERSERKER SAINT HIMSELF!
WHAT NOW, SON OF HERA? HAVE YOU COME TO CLAIM MY OTHER ARM?
"I HAVE NO DOUBT THE HULK DID NOT UNDERSTAND THE NATURE OF THE CONFLICT."
AND YOU SHALL EARN THE RIGHT TO FEAST ON MY KILL--
--ONLY BY STOPPING ME FROM REACHING DOWN AND RIPPING THE MEAT OUT YOUR THROATS!
"ALL HE KNEW WAS THAT THOSE WHO SHELTERED HIM WERE BEING THREATENED."
FLEE WHILE YOU CAN, MONGREL SPAWN OF SCIENCE!
THIS INSULT WAS YOUR HOSTS' ALONE, BUT YOU SHALL SHARE THEIR FATE IF YOU DO NOT STEP--
SHHKKSSHH!!
--ASIDE...?
WHAT WITCHERY...?

"AND THAT WAS ALL HE NEEDED TO KNOW!"
TAW--
--PRAWNNNCH
CRACK
RRAAAGHHH!!
KAPLACK!

SILENCE...CAN IT MEAN--IS IT POSSIBLE--
IT IS REAL, ZENO! OUR EMERALD FRIEND HAS FELLED TERRIBLE ARES!
PERHAPS IT--NO, IT MUST BE A SIGN FROM GAEA!

WELL DONE, COUSIN! BUT YOUR BATTLES HAVE ONLY JUST BEGUN!
THE WARLIKE OLYMPIANS WILL SOON KNOW ONE OF THEIR OWN HAS FALLEN-- THEY WILL NOT REST UNTIL THEY WREAK THEIR VENGEANCE ON ALL THREE OF US--

--UNLESS YOU TAKE THE FIGHT TO THEM!
TO MOUNT OLYMPUS! THERE! SEE?

THERE IS THE SEAT OF YOUR ENEMIES!
"THERE ARE THOSE WHO SAY MOUNT OLYMPUS, LIKE ANY OTHER HIGH, INACCESSIBLE HEAVEN, IS A METAPHOR FOR THE ARDUOUSNESS OF SPIRITUAL ENLIGHTENMENT.
RRRAAAARRRGGHH!!
YES, COUSIN, YES!
LEAVE NO OLYMPIAN LIVING!
"IF THAT'S TRUE, THEN THE HULK MUST BE THE MOST SPIRITUALLY CENTERED BEING ON THE PLANET.
RRRRAAAAAAAAHHH!!
"BECAUSE HE MADE IT TO THE TOP IN ONE JUMP."
SHALL I GIVE THE ORDER TO EVACUATE THE CITY, M'LORD--?
NEVER, HEBE!
WE CAN ONLY PRAY MY MESSENGER FOUND YOUR HUSBAND ON THE MORTAL PLANE, AND--

HULK, PLEASE!
THE OTHER GODS ARE FORMIDABLE SPARRING PARTNERS, TO BE SURE...
...BUT I ASK YOU, DO YOU VISIT MANHATTAN TO SEE THE SECOND TALLEST BUILDING, OR THE EMPIRE STATE?
WOULD YOU VIEW EVERY OTHER MASTERPIECE IN PARIS BUT THE MONA LISA?
LIKEWISE, IF YOU HAVE TRAVELED ALL THE WAY TO HIGH OLYMPUS TO DO BATTLE...
...IT WOULD SIMPLY BE RUDE TO ALLOW ANY OTHER THAN THE PRINCE OF POWER TO BESTOW UPON YOU...
RAAAAAAARRRGHHH!!
...THE GIFT!

THE GIFT OF COMBAT!
RUURRHH?
"A MORTAL PANKRATION FIGHTER CAN USE THE DOUBLE LEG TAKEDOWN TO DRIVE AN OPPONENT'S HEAD INTO THE GROUND WITH A 3,500 POUND IMPACT.
"WHEN HERCULES DOES IT...
KRAKABAKA
"IMAGINE BEING SLAMMED INTO THE SIDE OF A MOUNTAIN.
"BY A JUMBO JET.
"AT TOP SPEED.
"FLOWN BY A COKED-UP SOCIOPATH."
PLOORGGG!!
DO YOU YIELD?
WOK! CHOK! WOK! KRAK! PUNCH! BOP! CHOK! WOK! KRAK! WOK! WOK! WOK! PUNCH!
THOOP! TWIK! POK! WOK! PUNCH! WOK! WOK! WOK! KRAK! PUNCH! BOP! BOP! PUNCH!
MONSTER, I SAY...
...DO YOU YIELD?

GRRAAAAAGH!!
WHA--?

DID YOU--DID YOU JUST FLEX ME OFF YOUR BODY USING YOUR PECTORALS ALONE?
YOU ARE QUITE A SPECIMEN, CREATURE!
FOR A MOMENT THERE I FEARED YOU WOULD PUT UP EVEN LESS A FIGHT THAN DEMOLITION DUNPHY--

WHAT?
WHY ARE YOU
WHISPERING?
SPEAK
UP IF YOU
WANT ME
TO--

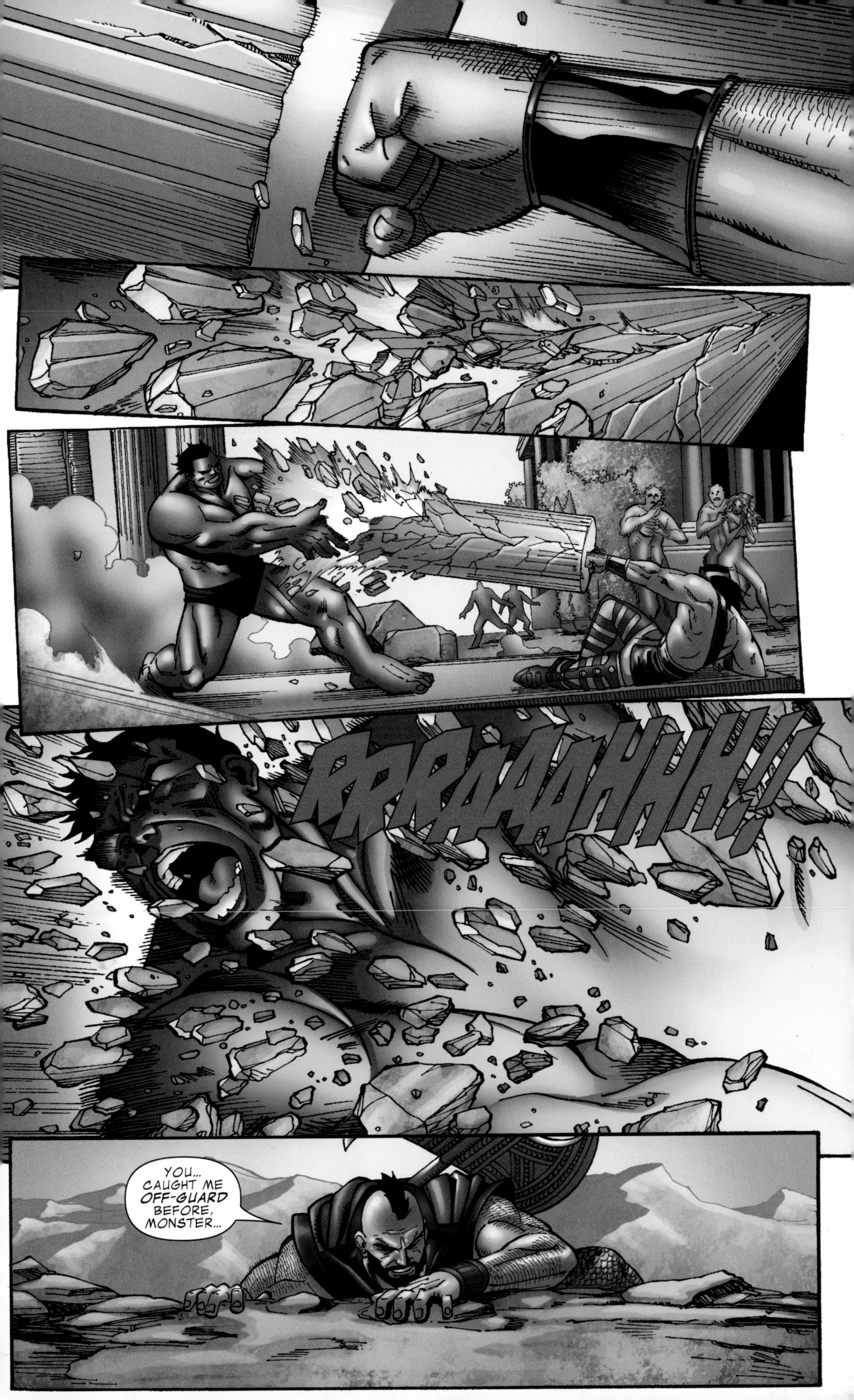
RRRAAAAHHH!!
YOU... CAUGHT ME OFF-GUARD BEFORE, MONSTER...

NOW I AM MORE THAN HAPPY TO RETURN THE FAVOR!
NAY!
ZWAAKK!
NO MAN-- NOR ARES--WILL STAIN MY HONOR BY TREACHEROUS ATTACKS ON AN ESTIMABLE FOE!

A WORD FROM THE WISE, LITTLE BROTHER:
'TWAS AN UNPROVOKED ATTACK BY ARES ON THE HULK'S GIANT FRIENDS THAT INSPIRED HIS RAMPAGE.
I'VE KNOWN YOU ONLY TO SPEAK THE TRUTH, SISTER ATHENA--
--AND SO, PERHAPS, THIS MATCH SHOULD BE SCORED A DRAW.

WHAT SAY YOU, MONSTER? DO YOU ACCEPT THE PLEDGE OF HERCULES THAT THE GOD OF WAR WILL NO MORE THREATEN YOU AND YOURS?
"FOR A MOMENT, IT LOOKED AS IF THE HULK WOULD ACCEPT THE LION OF OLYMPUS' OFFER.

"BUT THEN..."
SSSKRRRRRRREEEEE--

-EEEEEAAARRRRKKK--
-KRAAKOOOOM!
GRRRAAAAAA!
YES, MY CHILDREN. FIND YOUR BIG BROTHER ZEUS.
AND TELL HIM...
...PAPA'S HOME.
"AYE, T'WAS BLOODY CRONUS... FREE AT LAST...

"...AND READY TO WREAK TERRIBLE VENGEANCE ON THE USURPERS OF HIS THRONE."
LOOK BELOW, OLYMPIANS!
AND PREPARE TO DEFEND FATHER ZEUS!
NAY, BROTHER, LOOK ABOVE!
DEMOGORGE!
THIS IS A MERE FAMILY SPAT! YOU HAVE NO BUSINESS HERE!
GOD-EATER! GO BACK TO YOUR HOME IN THE SUN!
IF THE GIANTS WIN...
...IF OLYMPUS FALLS...
...THEN THE COSMIC AXIS SHIFTS.
AND THE GOD-EATER...
...FEASTS.

SHALL I KILL HIM FOR YOU, FATHER?
CLONK!
FOOL. HE ONCE ATE THE ELDER GODS THEMSELVES. IF HE STARTS AGAIN, HE COULD CONSUME THIS ENTIRE REALM AND THE HUMAN SPHERE IT ABUTS.
A WHELP LIKE YOU WOULD SCARCELY--
GRRRRAAAAA!
HARK, MY SONS. THIS HULK-THING IS RIGHT.
THE GIANTS BEGAN THIS FIGHT. NOW THEY MUST--
GAH!
FATHER!
YOUR BROTHER SAYS YOUR TIME AMONG THE HUMANS HAS MADE YOU SOFT.
PROVE HIM WRONG...

...AND BRING ME THE HEAD OF EVERY GIANT WHO STANDS AGAINST US!

SHHLANGG!
CAREFUL, COUSIN!
CRONUS SWINGS THAT THING AS IF HE WERE BLIND AS I!
THOUGH HOW HE COULD MISTAKE *YOUR* GREAT STINK...
...FOR THAT OF THE GODS--
UKKK--
GRRRAAAAAA!

CRONUS!
HERCULES! THE GOD-EATER COMES!
LET HIM!

WE GODS HAVE TRIUMPHED, DEMOGORGE!
YOU HAVE NO CLAIM HERE!
BUT IF IT'S A MEAL YOU WANT, I'VE GOT ONE TO STICK IN YOUR CRAW!
HA.
ALL IN GOOD TIME, LITTLE GOD.
ALL HAIL...
...HERCULES!
GIANT SLAYER! DEMON DEFIER! LION OF OLYMPUS!
AH, BUT I DID NOT DO IT ALONE!
TAKE MY HAND, OLD FRIEND...

...HULK...?
"THE SORCERER'S SPELL TOOK EFFECT...
"...SPIRITING THE HULK AWAY FROM YET ANOTHER WORLD HE COULD NEVER UNDERSTAND...
"...AND BACK TO HIS OWN DARK, ETERNAL PRISON."

I KNOW WHAT YOU'RE THINKING. YOU WANT TO MAKE EXCUSES FOR HIM. EVEN AS YOU DID FOR THE HULK.
HERCULES WAS BLIND WITH THE BATTLE, ET CETERA.
BUT ZEUS WOULD HAVE COMMANDED HIM TO KILL THEM REGARDLESS.
AND HERCULES, SON OF ZEUS, LION OF OLYMPUS...
...WOULD HAVE OBEYED.
YOU DON'T KNOW WHAT YOU'RE TALKING ABOUT.
AH. MY APOLOGIES. YOUR THREE WEEKS HAVE OF COURSE TAUGHT YOU FAR MORE THAN MY THREE MILLENNIA WITH MY BROTHER.
WHY...WHY ARE YOU TELLING ME THIS?
BECAUSE YOU CHOOSE TO WALK WITH TITANS, AMADEUS.
AND IF YOU ARE UNPREPARED TO ACCEPT THAT GODS MUST SOMETIMES BE MONSTERS...
...YOU COULD BRING DOOM UPON US ALL.
END.